THE LAST WORD ON
EXMOOR

Dedicated to Arthur

THE LAST WORD ON
EXMOOR

NORMA HUXTABLE

HALSGROVE

First published in Great Britain in 2001
Reprinted 2001

ISBN 1 84114 105 4

British Library Cataloguing-in-Publication Data
A CIP record for this title is available from the British Library

HALSGROVE
Halsgrove House
Lower Moor Way
Tiverton, Devon EX16 6SS
Tel: 01884 243242
Fax: 01884 243325
email sales@halsgrove.com
website www.halsgrove.com

Front cover illustration by Charles Wood

Printed and bound in Great Britain by The Cromwell Press, Trowbridge

Chapter One

To find Chilcott you drive on to Exmoor and turn left at the last tele-
graph pole. With no sign pointing to the farm, it always seems surprising that any visitors ever find us. Not with 240 square miles of
Exmoor spreading all around them, and a toss-up over which lane to
take. Plus the breathtaking views and/or cloud and mist just to add
to their distraction.

The reason there's no sign is that the hedge at the turn-off, half a
mile up the lane, belongs to the farmer next door, as decent a chap as
you would ever wish to meet. He lives at Higher Chilcott Farm. We
live just around the corner at Lower Chilcott Farm. Originally it
seemed just a formality to enquire if we might erect a sign pointing
jointly to 'Chilcott Farms', after all it was his hedge and it seemed
churlish not to include him in the directions. The effect on our quiet,
reasonable neighbour could not have been more dynamic if somebody had snipped him with the sheep shears. 'No, no, no!,' he trumpeted, his pipe falling to the ground as he wildly waved his arms. 'I
got enough chaps looking for me wanting money and wasting time
without a sign pointing to where I lives.' Well then, we pursued
soothingly, would he be against a direction solely to Lower Chilcott?
'Yes!' he shouted, ''cos if they time wasters sees Lower they'll work it
out that Higher got to be thereabouts and us'll never be shot of 'em.'
He looked directly at the Farmer/Husband/Boss, daring him to dis-
agree with this simple logic, who nodded, conceding that he had
made his point.

Although this might have discouraged a few half-hearted Sales
Reps, or even the Men from the Ministry on a busy day, it never
seemed to deter the farm guests, who treated it as a challenge,
zooming up and down the lanes with grim determination until they
finally, and usually accidentally, turned into our yard.

I would open the door of our farmhouse and usher the guests into
the flagstoned entrance hall-cum-cider-cellar, politely enquiring
about their journey. Not too much about the journey though, as they
had usually covered the distance from home to Exmoor in record
time and after that their problems started. To take their minds off it
I would launch into a brief history of the house, explaining how the
small, prison-like window at the back of the cider room with its iron
bars was installed in the sixteenth century for the purpose of keeping

the farm workers from breaking in and getting 'cidered-up' from the casks on their great oak stands. To be drunk, on Exmoor, is disgusting, but then nobody ever gets drunk. They get 'cidered-up' which is a different thing altogether, and perfectly respectable. Hereabouts I would usually pause to catch my breath after all the flow of information, and now and again I used to add proudly, 'This is a very old house,' but I stopped that after a lady scanned the old cider cellar with its heavy beams and uneven walls and smiled vaguely. 'You mustn't mind that, dearie,' she said kindly. 'You got to live where your work is. Can't all have new houses, can we?'

After showing the new guests their rooms, I usually left them relaxing in the sitting-room whilst I made tea. The old, established guests, or the Die-hards, as we called them, would sort out their own rooms, then follow me into the kitchen and range themselves on the long settle behind the kitchen table, but I quailed from letting loose new and sympathetic ladies in such an old kitchen. 'Flagstones, dearie? In a kitchen? Don't you know you can get them all evened out and nice Marley tiles laid? And you never do cooking on *that* old thing!' A searching glance round, then the follow-up. 'And where's your sink? I thought everybody in England got a sink!'

'This way, m'dears,' I told them, and led the way down two steps into the scullery where the sink stood over a 70 feet deep blocked-up well. I would explain how our water now comes from a spring up on the high moors, but refrained from mentioning at this early stage the lively little frogs and other fauna that they might find sharing their bath water. Even so, the spring water is beautiful, soft, blue and caressing. I once remarked on this to an old farmer who lived at Chilcott years ago, and was greatly taken aback by his scathing reply. ''Tis rubbish,' he said. 'My old cows gived better water than that.'

'Why ever do you say that, Mr Hooper?' I queried. ''Cos the water from my old well tasted just like gin!' he answered, licking his lips at the memory.

As we turned back into the kitchen I pointed out the dairy, which opened off at the far end; a large, cool and airy cellar-type room with built-in marble slabs and countless shelves, which housed two deep freezers, full of our own pigs, lambs and beef. By this time I sensed the ladies were doing a few time-and-motion sums, no doubt visualising me spending my day hopping, skipping and jumping from Rayburn cooker to sink to dairy and back again. Some even remarked on it and I would tell them what wonderful exercise it was, and all for free.

Preparing the tea, dropping clotted cream and strawberry jam on to warm scones, I would recall that we lived like this from choice, although it was never quite this way when we started. When the Farmer/Husband/Boss and I married, his father made over to us part of his farm in North Devon, and we were installed in a new and modern farmhouse. Father retired, and following old traditions, the family dwelling house and the bulk of the land was passed down to the eldest son, George. Although I accepted this as right and proper, I had shameful secret yearnings for the old residence and did my best to smother my ingratitude by comparing my easy-to-run modern home with the hard-working farmhouse.

However, I doubt if we should ever have moved had it not been for the summer visitors eventually crowding us out.

At first, they never even figured on our farm plan, but came about from sheer necessity. From the start we were dogged with continuous bad luck, and luck, whether it be good or bad, is something we super-stitious West Country folk treat with respect. Possibly some of our misfortune stemmed from being under-capitalised, and even with my father-in-law's help, it was a struggle to set up a small dairy unit. Wary of placing all our eggs in one basket, we bought a large sow called Minnie, who was to be the basis of a pig unit, but she caused so much damage to our own and our neighbours' property, that we ended up struggling to pay her debts as well as our own. The solution that Minnie should be packed off to market was out of the question, as by that time Minnie and me were Best Friends, a happy relationship that lasted until she died of old age. All the quarrels were between the frolicsome pig and the hot-headed Farmer/Husband/Boss, and as an onlooker I could see both sides of their arguments, with the farmer furious at his doors and fences being bulldozed down, and the pig vicious at heavy missiles suddenly clouting her snout just as she was investigating something new and interesting.

Besides Minnie, we seemed to be breaking all the old farming rules about not carrying passengers, by building up a small posse of dependants. There was the sheepdog and the farm cat, who admit-tedly both worked for their living, and a sickly white calf rescued when a gale demolished our lean-to barn, together with a small deformed hen called Gladys, who never laid an egg in her life. All thriving on the best of everything on our miniscule income.

The crunch came in April, not from the animals but from the price of a pair of stockings. I was reduced to asking the Farmer/ Husband/Boss for money for a new pair and he jibbed at it, obstinately, saying I'd only had a pair at Christmas and 'what had become of they?' In a blinding flash I saw a lifetime of requests and refusals stretching ahead. Something had to be done. I knew our flagging income needed an injection of, I wasn't sure what, but something completely divorced from farming, if only until our luck changed. A job away from the premises was out of the question, as back in those days, and up to as recently as ten years ago, farmers' wives and daughters *never left* the farm. The womenfolk were there to look after the menfolk, and the daughters helped Mother do just that, with marriage the goal and escape being the start of their own private treadmill, as few married out of farming. The wife not only had to be seen to be there, but seen to be busy, even if she were only walking across the yard carrying a bucket.

My thoughts wandered round the neighbours and finally stopped at two farms, side by side, a couple of miles down the road. They both had carpet on the stairs. They both took summer visitors. Back then, nobody had one without the other. The carpet was always a give-away as soon as you stepped inside a place that went in for holiday letting, otherwise only townsfolk could afford such luxury. The more I considered this, the more it appealed. Not so much the carpeting, as trying to make some sort of living for us all. Even so, I could see snags in the idea, for although the cooking appealed, the notion of spending long hours indoors, did not. Telling myself severely that ready cash in the form of a pay-day every Saturday, was not going to happen without sacrifices, I set off there and then to tell my thoughts to the Farmer/Husband/Boss.

It was well-timed as he had just finished milking and was letting out our few cows on to the early spring grass. I helped to unchain the last two, and then, leaning against the dairy wall, I tentatively brought up my proposition for summer visitors. He was not impressed.

'Seven hundred and twenty years of Huxtables, Maid, and every one a farmer,' he testified, latching his thumbs in his braces and rocking gently against the outside wall. 'And now you'm wanting to change history.'

'Nobody's asking you not to farm,' I told him. ''Tis what you might call a slight change of direction, more a sideline, really. And it wouldn't be forever, only 'til us get back on our feet.'

It didn't surprise me that my man was stoically prepared to sail on unaided in the hope of weathering the storm, farmers having an in-built optimism for fighting the elements, disease and poor crops. I watched him scan the panoramic horizon spread below our North Devon farm, letting his gaze rest on the chimney stacks of his birth place, nestled in a hollow a couple of fields away. He was dubious. 'I dunno' that I want a lot of ol' visitors about the place. I can't fancy screamin' kids and folks shoutin' an' singin'. 'Twould drive a fellow cracky.'

I kicked at the grass with my boot, and admitted he had a point. 'I don't fancy it quite like that myself,' I told him. 'P'raps more sort of quiet and peaceful like. More of a restful holiday.' There was a lengthy pause as my partner took off his cap and thoughtfully scratched his head. When he spoke it was with a hint of wavering uncertainty.

'Well, Maid, 'tis up to you,' he said slowly. 'I don't want no part of it. If you think you can manage, fair enough, but you'm not getting me involved in any capers with visitor folks. I got other things to think about.'

This was true enough, and I knew that if I had not actually got his blessing, it was the nearest I was ever likely to get to a go-ahead.

Not knowing where to start, I decided to seek advice from the two farmers' wives with the carpet, down the road. They were kindly ladies generously giving me the benefit of their successful knowledge from start to finish. I must, they stressed, commence with an adver-tisement in *Daltons Weekly*, a publication I had hitherto never heard of, and I should offer bed, breakfast and evening dinner. All the profit came from the B&B, and all the hard slogging was with the dinner, but I would have to accept that holidaymakers don't relish motoring miles in the country looking for their dinner.

It was vital they told me, to go at once to the nearest Newsagent, who would give me a form to fill out for *Daltons Weekly*, which would be sent off with my remittance, and then I must delay all preparations until my advertisement appeared to see if I received any enquiries. My neighbours' caution was based on the lateness of the advertise-ment, after all it was already April, and most holidaymakers consid-ered all the best places to be sold out by the end of January. So it could be doubtful, the ladies pointed out, if anything would be left for me at such a late date.

At the newsagents I carefully printed my advertisement in block capitals on an official form and handed over 12s., which paid for three insertions. The proper charge was 6s. per week, but this was a special end-of-season offer, with three insertions for the price of two. Despite my neighbours' uncertainty, coupled with the newspaper's suspicious generosity, my morale was running high. I have never parted with money more willingly. This, I thought, could surely be the turning point of our bad luck. If the offer had not been such a good one, I might have been tempted to ask the newsagent for a couple of coppers back for 'luck money'. After all, no farming deal is ever completed without a small return of cash to the buyer for good luck. Perhaps, I thought optimistically, mine would come with the publication of my advertisement in three weeks' time.

The weeks passed slowly, though not without incident. One of our Friesian cows went down with grass staggers but, miraculously, survived, and my Best Friend, Minnie, visited next door and demolished a brood of eggs due to hatch the following day. Our neighbours' two hundred sheep paid us a reciprocal visit through the gap Minnie had bulldozed in the hedge. Gladys, the little hen, scratched busily in the newly planted seed beds, whilst Daisy May, the sickly white calf, took a turn for the better and showed her gratitude by licking my face at every opportunity. The actual process was not so much like licking as having the yard broom drawn slowly and agonisingly across my cheeks, so painful a torture it brought tears to my eyes, but it pleased Daisy May to be affectionate, so I tended to encourage her.

At long last, a copy of *Daltons Weekly* finally arrived, with my advertisement ringed in red crayon, amongst several other like offerings on the same page. Incredibly, my laboriously printed, carefully worded epistle was reduced to what looked like a coded message in an agony column. B&B, ED and H&C, whilst some had even more mysterious codes. One was S.I.M. which I later found out stood for Spring Interior Mattresses, though one landlady, determined not to be abbreviated, had left out the 'Spring' prefix so that her advertisement succeeded to read in full 'Interior Mattresses'. This I could see conjuring up to holidaymakers' visions of likely exterior mattresses with bodies strewn on them round the yard every night.

Fortunately, our fears over the lateness of the advertising were unfounded, as enquiries for holidays started to arrive daily. Some of them appeared to be better informed than myself, and even wrote in the same code as the newspaper.

'We would like B&B, E.D. etc.' and one letter even added another, more complex twist to puzzle my already bemused brain. 'Do you have a W.C.?' I didn't know. Ashamed to show my ignorance to the Farmer/Husband/Boss, I passed the letter to him across the breakfast table, hoping he might de-code it. He read it, frowning, then handed it back, saying, 'Wat's a W.C., Maid?'

Fired with inspiration, I answered casually, 'Why, 'tis a Wesleyan Chapel.' But as I wrote the reply it somehow sounded all wrong. 'Yes, certainly we have a W.C., just three miles away in the village...' Mercifully, common sense prevailed when I realised the cautious holidaymakers had obviously stayed in the country before and were just checking on the amenities.

I accepted every booking it was possible to squeeze in, on a simple basis of first come, first served. There was no discrimination whatsoever. I wanted everybody. Little did the would-be visitors know that the rooms they were jostling with one another to book, described in my letter as 'Pleasant and Comfortable', did not, at that time, even sport beds, let alone such little refinements as curtains and blankets. Just as soon as their trusting deposits started arriving, I took off on a round of the local sale rooms, farm sales, house sales, anywhere with anything to sell.

The weeks flew by in a flurry of preparation and a shower of advice from my neighbouring landladies, the bulk of which I seized on, noted and eventually put into practice. *One said*, 'You got to save on your butter, my dear. Put it in the fridge overnight and 'twill go so hard they won't be able to spread it in the morning.' As I was only buying essentials, not luxuries like fridges, this did not strictly apply.

Something for nothing appeals to everybody, so NO EXTRAS. Fix a price to cover everything from baths and morning tea through to bedtime cocoa. Then they can budget exactly for their holiday.

No seaside boarding-house type notices plastered in every room. Not one. Anywhere. It is not a hotel, you are inviting these people to share your home, and you want them to feel relaxed and comfortable, and above all welcome.

Fill 'em up on taters and bread pudden. Remember, a full guest is a happy guest!

Make sure the kids don't wet the beds. More complex advice, this, my finer feelings rebelling at a midnight round-up of suspect bed-wetters, form fours and quick march to the lavatory.

Keep smiling was obvious, I thought, but at that time I simply did not foresee a lifetime stretching ahead when the body, face and the smile all crumpled in a heap behind the kitchen door every midnight.

Before my first guests were due to arrive, my kindly landlady neighbours came to inspect my efforts. One or two minor adjustments were made before they realised the biggest essential of all was missing. A Visitors Book. To my mind this was strictly against the hotel image we were trying to play down, but no, they insisted, it was good business to keep a visitors book which all guests signed with their names and addresses before leaving. Then, at Christmas, I must send them all a greetings card and that would jog their memory for next year's holiday. This made good business sense, but the only book the local Newsagent had in stock looked far too grand for our simple farm. It was satin-bound in peacock blue, with the word 'Visitors' engraved in flourishing gilt script on the cover. Worst of all, the price was an astronomic 8s.6d. which smacked of wilful extravagance for a mere notebook, remembering the wardrobes bought for 7s.6d. and chests of drawers for only 5s.

Reluctantly, I parted with the money, although by then I had hit rock bottom and it seemed everything was conspiring to knock me where it hurt most, which was in the pocket. Little did I think then that Visitors Book would turn out to be my best-ever buy. It is full of witticisms, cartoons cut from newspapers, photographs and prose and poems that budding literary geniuses have lain awake at night to compose, before appearing, bleary-eyed, on a Saturday morning to write up their masterpiece. One regretful departing guest wrote, 'Never knew life among the peasants could be so jolly!' whilst a blonde lady from Redhill became immortalised with her heartfelt offering, 'Bollocks and ta'.

Small wonder, when in the depths of winter and on a poor T.V. night the Farmer/Husband/Boss instructed, 'Turn that twaddle off, Maid, and let's read the Visitors Book.'

Chapter Two

When the great day in June dawned for my first guests' arrival, all my former self-confidence ebbed. I willed the telephone to ring with an excuse, any excuse, for their cancellation. Measles would have been a good one, or 'flu, or even just plain changed their minds. I didn't care, being overcome with the enormity of my undertaking. Then I groaned and remembered the spent deposits and knew there could be no turning back.

It was to be a very gentle start, with just four people, comprising two couples from London who would be travelling together and had written to say they hoped to arrive about four in the afternoon. Well, I determined, one thing they would never learn was that they were to be my first guests. I would stride out to greet them wearing a well-seasoned landlady look that boded no nonsense. What sort of nonsense they might get up to I had not the faintest idea. I was new to the trade; young, naive and dead ignorant.

The panic stayed with me all day, and if anything, increased as the four o'clock deadline approached. I felt hot and cross, particularly with the Farmer/Husband/Boss from whom I had hoped for some crumbs of comfort and who had merely dismissed my fears with a curt, 'Well, if you don't think you can manage it, you should'n took it on.'

When the car drew up outside, soon after four, I catapulted myself out the door, whizzing proof that I could, and would, cope. The new guests could see from the newly painted sign that they were at the right farm, but as I ran to greet them I was completely shattered by the kindly looking lady's very first remark as she wound down the car window.

'Good afternoon, dear, is your mummy home?' I could feel my face flushing with embarrassment as I explained that I was, in fact, their landlady, whilst they looked as though they would give the earth to escape in the opposite direction at 90 miles per hour, with, 'I bet she can't cook', written all over their faces. They were wrong, I could cook, having taught myself, and my mother-in-law had long since ceased sending over cold slabs of rice pudding to keep us going.

As I ushered in my captive first guests it occurred to me, fleetingly, that the situation had its lighter side. There I had been worrying about them, whilst they in turn were obviously horrified when they realised that I was to be their landlady. However, they seemed pleased with the accommodation; they chatted over their first cup of tea, turned out to be good eaters, and what might have been a tricky situation soon resolved itself.

I was off to a flying start with four easy-going people, and before their week had ended I had told them what they must indeed have guessed from the very beginning, that they were my very first guests. It was quite a wrench the following Saturday when they were due to leave and my first change-over arrived. Since then I have often dreaded the change-over day. It can be quite difficult parting from people with whom you forge an easy-going friendship, and replacing them with other unknowns. Over the years I have learnt to be flippant with the goodbyes.

'Answer us truthfully,' they demand. 'Do you really miss us after we're gone?'

'Certainly,' I reply. 'But counting your money helps take the sting out of parting.'

My first guests paid up just before they left on the Saturday morning. They paid for much the same then as they do now. Only the price differed. For their money I gave them morning tea at eight, comprising a tray of tea with biscuits, followed by the traditional farm breakfast at nine, with a choice of cereal, prunes or apricots and jugs of creamy milk from our Jersey cow. This is followed by bacon, eggs, tomatoes and fried potatoes, toast and home-made marmalade, tea or coffee.

The dinner at night might be home-made soup (or fresh melon or some similar light starter, depending on the meal), then the main course of, for example, home-roast lamb with its accompaniments (or steak and kidney pie made with flaky pastry, or possibly a nice fresh trout), potatoes in various guises, and usually a green vegetable and a root vegetable. This was followed by home-made dessert, topped with clotted cream (kind permission of the Jersey cow again) and could vary from an old-fashioned suet pud to a lemon syllabub or cherry cheesecake. Dinner was always rounded off with biscuits and the cheeseboard, tea or coffee. On Sundays we always had dinner about two in the afternoon, which gave guests a chance to sample the local cider beforehand and spend the rest of the afternoon sleeping it off until Sunday night supper at 7.30.

For this, all those years ago, my first visitors paid me £4 10s. per person, per week. And on top of that, to my great surprise, they gave me a whole pound for myself. I can remember fluttering £17 (they had paid £2 deposit) through my disbelieving fingers, just revelling in the feel of all that money. The F/H/B joined me, marvelling at so much money, recalling the days up to our marriage when he had collected £1 a week wages from his farmer father. And now somebody had actually *given* us a whole pound, just like that!

Since those very early days, people's generosity has never ceased to overwhelm me. We have had pictures painted for us, our garden weeded, and even beautiful material supplied by a cloth manufacturer to keep us clothed in a manner to which we were certainly never before accustomed.

I discovered quite soon that I could ruthlessly take advantage of lady guests by parading the Farmer/Husband/Boss across the yard disguised as a bundle of rags. I get a mental block when it comes to knitting and sewing and find it a lot easier to skin a rabbit than to sew on a button. With the happy result that lady guests take pity on my walking bundle of rags and attempt to string him together again. Then they go home and knit him a nice new sweater in place of his shrunken Marks & Spencer model.

Once only do I recall being smitten with conscience and that was when I spotted him fighting against a howling gale with his buttonless leather jerkin billowing out behind him like inflated angels' wings, as though he were about to take off for the Great Farm in the Sky any minute. It was mid-winter and there were no sympathetic lady holidaymakers to call on. It was up to me, and that night I searched out the four biggest buttons I could find from a jam jar full that had arrived from my mother-in-law like a dowry. It was sweated labour, sewing those buttons on that tough old leather jerkin, but I said nothing, wanting it to come as a lovely surprise.

To my chagrin, the next day there he was again, still into his heavenly angels' act, with his jerkin unbuttoned and billowing back-side-on. Furious that my night's labour of love had gone unnoticed, I flew down the yard and shrieked over the gale, 'Button your buttons!'

'No, *you* button 'em,' came the ungracious reply. Whereupon I seized the small farmer and attempted to do just that, realising as I struggled, that the buttons were half as big again as the buttonholes. In my mind big buttonholes equalled big buttons and I hadn't bothered to try them for size. The poor, neglected man had only to recount this and other like stories to sympathetic lady guests to get them all lined up on his side, vying one with the other to sew him together.

I've got to be the winner here, but human nature being what it is, I cannot resist chipping in spitefully about his retaliatory shots at carpentry and how, when it comes to measurement, he is as vague as myself. Like when he decided to knock up a rustic archway for the garden. He built it on the lawn but when the two of us hoisted it into position it towered high above the roof of the house. He was bent over the gigantic archway sawing off half of its legs, when a couple of friends from the village called, and they fell about with helpless laughter. I joined in until I realised it was not altogether the rustic archway that tickled them quite as such as the colourful patch cobbled on the backside of the F/H/B's breeches.

Whilst lady sewers come two-a-penny, carpenters are decidedly thin on the ground and though handy-men are free enough with their advice, they don't always actually volunteer to do anything. Correction. One would-be carpenter repaired a chair in the sitting-room, in fact he did several jobs, none of which lasted more than a couple of days. He left on the Saturday so consequently was not present to undertake any responsibility for what happened to the new arrivals as a result of his workmanship.

The F/H/B showed them into the sitting-room whilst I made their tea. Five minutes later he re-appeared in the kitchen, urging me to leave everything and make a dash at the double for the other room where a minor crisis was taking place. It seemed he had no sooner sat Grandma in my handyman's newly repaired chair than he could see her slowly, an inch at a time, sinking through to the floor. Perhaps, suggested the F/H/B, I might tactfully persuade her to sit elsewhere before she realised her danger. Too late, Grandma had sunk too far to ever get out unaided. She was a large lady and the lower she sank, the tighter she wedged. In the end it was all hands on deck, with pushers behind the chair and pullers in front, all of us united in our efforts to free Grandma, who, I could tell, as a first-time visitor, was not impressed with our standards. Exaggeration crept in, with the old lady remarking grumpily that if her time was up she'd as soon go in her own bed as somebody else's house. It marked the start of one of our less successful weeks.

The one person who was delighted at the turn of events was the F/H/B, as this drew a parallel with his own efforts at repairs, to which he gleefully admitted. Every handyman I have ever rounded up is branded as a 'creep', sneaking the job my small, obstinate farmer is just about to tackle. Perhaps his greatest triumph was not the sitting-room chair but the bathroom mirror, which I had talked yet another handyman into hanging. That mirror had been hanging about for six months when my new handyman carried it into the bathroom, assuring me it was only a ten-minute job. It took less than that. With his first, deft blow he put his hammer straight through it and his first reflex action was to lock himself in the bathroom with the shattered mirror, whilst the distressed wife and I pleaded with him to come out. Eventually he did come out but not until dinner time. We found out afterwards that he was accident prone so I thought it best to cross him off my list of handymen.

New hairdressers, too, were a boon and they always seemed to enjoy their job so much that I felt I was doing them a favour by letting them restore some shape and order to my flyaway hair, even though they were supposed to be on holiday. Shampoos and sets were usually carried out with the minimum of hassle, though a little problem did arise once when the hairdryer went up in a puff of blue smoke. Time being of great importance, my hairdresser took off to the next farm to borrow one. To hurry things on a bit I was inspired to open the oven door of the solid fuel cooker and stick my head inside. By the time my hairdresser returned with the dryer I had revolved two or three times in different positions, on my side, on my knees, and even sitting on the flagstones with my head tilted back into the oven. When she whipped off the little silky scarf covering the rollers she let fly a scream that could be heard two fields away.

The sizzling murmur that I had noticed when I was in the oven and had taken to be the kettle simmering on top, turned out to be my rollers melting in the intense heat. The pink and blue rollers had turned into pink and blue plastic hair. It took two hours of pulling and cutting to leave me with something that looked like a punk crewcut, with long intervals for the distressed hairdresser to wring her hands and exclaim dearie me, she had never seen anything like it in her life. It certainly did not bother me nearly as much as it did her, as beauty you have never had you never miss. I was born ugly. Perhaps hatched is the word. Perhaps my hair is my only good feature, but put all together and the overall effect is depressing. But the disastrous hair-do (for which I had nobody to blame but myself) really did not matter to me very much, though I finished up reviving my shocked hairdresser with Alka-Seltzer.

We soon found out with our guests that it paid to let them follow their own profession when on holiday, rather than try to turn them into farmers. Working on the land can be a disaster for an unfit townsman, though some just never give up and stick at it until they drop. One would-be farmer actually did drop after a few hours humping hay bales, so much so that he had to be helped up the stairs to his bed, where he stayed for the next three days. He was a dark, slim, frail looking sales rep. for Toilet Accessories, and had spent several holidays with us but the F/H/B had always managed to divert him from helping on the farm. Our past experience is usually a pointer to what the outcome is likely to be.

But on this particular holiday our man in toilet accessories was not so easily fobbed off. By eight o'clock every morning he was dressed in shorts and singlet, every inch an athlete as he headed for the yard to commence a strenuous routine of on-the-spot running and knees-bend, arms-stretch exercises. He told us he had been attending gym classes and taking sauna baths for weeks in preparation for this holiday, which had prepared him for days in the field working 'Shoulder to shoulder, man to man, don'tcha know!' And so he did, for exactly three hours. It was unfortunate that the hay bales that year were fairly green so would have been extra heavy. This coupled with a poor weather forecast to speed things up further all contributed to our toilet-accessory man's collapse.

I could not help but feel sympathetic when he was brought back from the field pale and exhausted and all but thrown into the kitchen by the F/H/B, as casually as he might throw in a rabbit for the pot. I helped him up to his room where he crept into bed, leaving me to discover it was only the use of his limbs that he had lost and not his appetite. I toiled up and down the stairs with trays of food, bearing out my secret theory that it was food and not so much exercise that our man needed. His features soon looked less pinched and the unhealthy paleness was slowly replaced with what looked like living tissue. He was so stiff I had to help him to sit up in bed, cluck-clucking sympathetically when he remarked ruefully that every little inch of him was aching, right to the tips of his fingers (from the prickles in the hay). This all served to reinforce the F/H/B's already dim view of what he termed artificial exercise.

'Bloody lot of nonsense,' he growled. 'Sauna baths and gymnastics. Give a chap a couple of hours labouring and you'll soon find who's fit and who ain't.' I nodded in total agreement as I set about my patient's lunch of pork chops in cider, fresh vegetables, and junket and cream.

Even so, a farm presents a real fascination for would-be workers, and whilst it is all very well for us to think they might be better off following their own profession, there cannot be a lot going for a toilet accessory salesman at Lower Chilcott Farm. Or for a London bus driver, for that matter, or a Post Office official, or a Formation Dancer, but they all numbered among our guests.

Chapter Three

Newcomers to the country are always ripe for speculation as to their business and whilst some could be a dead give-away from the moment they first present themselves, others need to be encouraged to talk about their work to assuage our inborn inquisitiveness. A newspaper report once showed a picture of Prince Charles mingling in a crowd, the caption stating that 'He is the only person in Britain who can ask people their occupation.' Wrong.

The Farmer/Husband/Boss, after all queries and hints failed to elicit the necessary information, would wade in with, 'And what might you do for a living, then?' One who had us foxed was a dignified elderly gentleman who fairly exuded quiet charm through his cherubic appearance. We spent half the week hazarding guesses over his profession. I thought perhaps a doctor as they are often reluctant to mention medicine as it results in them being bombarded with people's ailments. The F/H/B suspected someone even more reticent, possibly on a higher level than us mere mortals, like a parson. 'Might be a bleddy bishop fer all us know,' he said. 'Hang on a minute, Maid, I'll go and ask,' and he was through the door into the dining room, grim determination in every line.

The guests were still seated round the breakfast table, idly chatting and puffing at their cigarettes. The F/H/B joined in the conversation generally, finishing by poring over their maps and giving directions for rides and walks across the moors. In ones and twos they filed out until the courtly gentleman and his quiet little wife were the only ones left. Our man did not beat about the bush.

'What do you do for a living, then?' he demanded, daring the mystery guest not to answer. The reply came courteously and without hesitation.

'I'm a crook.'

'What's a crook?'

'You know – a crook. Actually, a fence for stolen property. I do very well at it. I've never actually been inside, but I've been arrested and got away with it. Had some narrow escapes though, I can tell you. Once when I had a pocketful of gold watches...' And after that initial revelation there was no stopping him as he regaled us with stories of close encounters with the police and life in his criminal underworld.

We listened fascinated to the gentle tones of the soft-spoken man who was costing us thousands to keep on the wrong side of the law. Although we do not possess any valuables of our own, my mind did become slightly worried when I thought of the other guests being under the same roof as a criminal. He must have read my thoughts because his little round features broke into a beatific smile as he said reassuringly, 'Never mix business with pleasure, my dear. It's just a job, you know, the same as they' – he waved a hand in the direction of the departed guests – 'have jobs.'

I could not quite convince myself of this, try as I would, particularly before our crook left and came into the kitchen for a confidential word over a possible business deal.

'Now then,' he said. 'Is there anything you want for the farm? Because if there is, just say so. Getting hold of stuff's no problem in my business, and if I can do anybody a good turn...' The kindly smile flashed on and off, 'Just say the word.'

'Yes,' said the F/H/B, a shade recklessly, to my startled mind. 'Yes, I could do with a bit of fencing for the fields.'

'You're on lad, you're on,' replied our crook generously. 'Soon's I get it I'll be on the blower.'

'You're nuts,' I told my man later. 'You ought to know better than getting mixed up with that sort of rubbish.'

'Geed 'ome,' he answered, ''ee'll never git ort like that up London,' but even as he said it he looked a trifle uneasy. And a fortnight later our crook came up with the goods, ringing to ask if we were still of the same mind about the fencing because he had a lorry on hand, loaded, and with delivery guaranteed the same day. The F/H/B hastily back-pedalled when it came to the crunch of having a lorry load of stolen goods arriving on his property.

'Serve you right,' I told him, seeing how shaken he was. 'Serve you right, you should never have gone along with it in the first place.' And I fixed my holier-than-thou expression just to make sure he knew I had notched one up on him at last.

On the right side of the law, we had a number of country-loving policemen holidaying here. With a little encouragement they could usually be persuaded to regale us with tales of the Big City, of dark deeds on dark nights, of dripping corpses being winched from the Thames, all riveting stuff which somehow made the hitherto fortnightly treat of our mobile library with its detective fiction pale by comparison. There is nothing to rival a real detective with a sense of the dramatic, telling his fearful stories at dead of night.

This leads me to one of the 'perks' of being a landlady, and that is of chatting to the guests and listening to their stories of their vastly different lives. Quite a lot of time is accounted for in this way, and we looked on it as an education, a bonus we could never otherwise have on our remote Exmoor farm. We both benefited hugely, and I cannot help but recall that years ago if the F/H/B encountered a stranger, he would cut corners to avoid him. Nevertheless, from this dubious beginning he has emerged as a top public relations man (my only one), checked only now and again by what he calls his outspokenness and what I call tactlessness.

After breakfast each morning our P.R. man would enquire of the guests in which direction they intended to travel should they decide to take a trip out, then, map in hand, he would plot them a course across the moors, off the beaten track and through the best scenery. It was very noticeable that although they all persist in their hatred of organised holidays, they gratefully accepted directions on spending their days, even to visiting ancient monuments and museums. Our P.R. man decided, quite rightly, that people do not visit Exmoor for shopping expeditions and the guests soon realised that the word 'shopping' did not come into his curriculum. In fact, it was best left unmentioned, being what he called 'for they folks with nort better to do.'

Often in the evening our P.R. man carried his coffee into the dining room and joined the visitors in their after-dinner chat, usually mulling over the day's events on the farm and their adventures on the moor. They tell us that Exmoor seems curiously shut off from reality and the Great Outside, almost as if it is cocooned in a little world of its own, exempt from the worries of the rest of the universe.

Conversation did not always flow naturally, and this is where my P.R. man showed his mettle. I propelled him through that dining-room door with straight-forward instructions to liven 'em up. ''Tis like a morgue in there,' I'd say. Sometimes they anticipated his arrival and got off to a flying start, whilst now and again it was heavy going. Nevertheless, it was one thing to jolly them along and quite another to be so outspoken at times that they visibly quaked. I well remember two of the guests tapping on the kitchen door one morning after breakfast, saying they would not be in for dinner that night. Our P.R. man fixed them with narrowed eyes as he looked up from his breakfast, his fork speared with a square of fried bread jabbing in their direction.

'What's the matter?' he demanded. 'Ain't our bloody food good enough for 'ee?' They both looked as though they wished they could turn into little mice and shrink away into the nearest mousehole. Whilst these people were new and fairly sedate – which most of them are to start with, anyway – some of the more established visitors (the Die-hards, we call them) would have given as good as they got, setting off a good-humoured slanging match with plenty of muck-slinging from both sides. One couple went so far as to write in the Visitors Book, 'Can't wait for next year when we knock on your door and hear these welcoming words, "Come in you Buggers".' At the other extreme someone wrote, 'Only one place is better than this, but you have to die first!'

The fun and the repartee were all part of the pattern of taking holidaymakers and although the chat was all part and parcel of the day's work, it did help along the hours. It must be quite certain that no trade union would ever accept a landlady's membership, such are the phenomenal working hours. Sixteen hours a day, seven days a week equals one hundred and twelve hours of solid slog. For months on end, because this is Exmoor not the coast, and the winter on Exmoor is very nearly as popular as the summer with the walking, riding, hunting and the famous moorland skies to gaze at throughout.

Holidaymakers tend to arrive in these parts at all times of the year, often exhausted from their $37^1/2$-hour week. And I believe them. They lead sedentary lives, with little or no exercise, their only relaxation being slumped in front of the telly at night; their jobs are often taxing and worrying, resulting in mental exhaustion which is very different from the physical exhaustion we feel after a day's work. Their appetites are often impaired, mainly I should think from a lack of fresh air, and they live on 'junk' food because it is quick and it stands to reason they are not going to arrive home late in the evening and start to cook a three-course dinner. Then, the next morning, something quick for breakfast and they are off again, sometimes with a two-hour journey stretching ahead before they even arrive at their work. Which makes it extra good to see them on holiday sitting down and relaxing over their farmhouse meals.

It is always noticeable how new guests tend to eat up fairly quickly and leave the table, whilst the Die-hards linger, smoking and chatting, especially at night. The deadline had to be 11 o'clock, when I shouted 'Time's up!' and slapped down the cornflake boxes for tomorrow's breakfast. To get to bed by midnight was doing very well, and the worst thing that could happen late at night was for a guest to come into the kitchen at four minutes to twelve and say pityingly 'Oh, you do look tired,' then sit down and engage in animated conversation until twenty to one. Then, glancing at the time, 'Oh dear, I suppose I had better let you get off to bed, I expect you have to get up at five – you do on farms, don't you?'

By that time I sometimes longed to say, 'Madam, I have just worked a 16-hour day. Neither you nor anybody else is going to turn it into a 20-hour day.' But I never did, reminding myself that the customer is always right. It surprises me sometimes just how little sleep kept me going, sometimes I think I cannot be quite normal and it worries me slightly. Well, as much as anything worries me, which is not a lot. I always have the winter and hibernation to look forward to.

Of the whole week, Saturdays and Sundays were the busiest, Saturday being the accepted change-over day, and on Sundays we had three meals, breakfast at nine, dinner at two and supper in the evening at seven-thirty. Even so, Sunday was my night off, as once the supper was over the washing up was quickly despatched, comprising just a plate, cup and saucer per person.

Sometimes, on a fine Sunday evening the two of us would take to the moors and indulge in our favourite relaxation, which was deer spotting. Exmoor is the home of the wild red deer and nothing quickens the pulse more than to pick out a herd of deer, or even a single grazing stag, in the twilight of a fine summer evening. We might walk across the moor over the heather and watch the lights come on in far-distant farmhouses and as dusk descends on a clear night the flashing signal from Hartland Point light-house outlines the far North Devon coastline.

Some Sundays I got my weekly airing from just walking round the farm, usually accompanied by a dog or two, and most certainly with the five ginger cats strung out untidily behind me. We headed down over the fields, watched buzzards swoop from the sky and herons fly lazily down the valley and listened to partridge chattering in the heather. When it became too dark to see any more, I whistled up the animals and turned for home. They were usually following their own pursuits by then, rabbiting or mousing, so I often arrived back with less than I started with.

Even then, my Sunday treat was not yet over because once the kitchen flagstones were washed and the breakfast and morning tea tray laid, I spread the Sunday newspapers on the big kitchen table and drank my Treat of the Week, a gigantic Pimm's No. 1. I can only blame my own visitors for my Sunday evening lapse into alcoholism. I used to be perfectly happy with a cup of cocoa until a couple of guests presented me with a complete Pimm's kit on my birthday, some years ago. There was the basic bottle, another of lemonade, a bag of apples and oranges and a sprig of mint, and I have never looked at a cup of cocoa since, furthermore any friends who drop in on a summer's evening are likely to be persuaded to try one of my 'specials' – a glorious mixture of alcohol, ice, strawberries, peaches and grapes. So popular did these become that the local off-licence reported booming business in Pimm's No. 1, no doubt evened out by a corresponding drop in cocoa sales.

My quiet moment of the week on Sunday evenings was usually spent alone, the ever gregarious F/H/B choosing to spend his leisure evening with the visitors in the sitting room, playing crib or scrabble. We both agreed, however, that this set us up for the week ahead although Monday, after the frantic weekend, always seemed like a little haven of tranquillity.

As the season wore on we would get into August and the dreaded school holidays, a month of screaming kids to be endured with gritted teeth when even the Pimm's flagged and lost some of its punch in reviving an all but clapped-out landlady. A little extra boost was deemed necessary, so I would slip on my ever-ready wellies, grab a torch and head for the fields. Counting to the third rabbit hole on the left I would reach in my arm and haul out my tin box, carefully laying it on the grassy bank. Then came the one pick-me-up that never failed, I counted the money.

Exmoor is the home of the wild red deer, who roam the moors elegant and graceful, fleet of foot and untamed as the moor itself. It is also the home, some say, of our wild women, also roaming the moors and equally untamed. This is acceptable until they are caught by Exmoor men, stern, Victorian, unrelenting, who set about their taming.

As most visitors view the area in the holiday season, when all the locals are engaged in their own various occupations, it often seems to surprise them if they hear that the calm, slow, easy-going life in the country is not quite all it appears to be. If they scratch the surface just a little, the revelations can be surprising, to say the least. An instance of this came in one of our late-night chats with our visitors when a certain lady was holding everybody spell-bound with a description of her recent visit to Italy. Particularly riveting was her account of the Italian male. 'The men,' she said, 'are disgusting. They grab women in the street, right there in front of everybody, pinch their bum and say they wanta make-a-da love. Have you *ever* heard of anything so degrading?'

'What a lot of bloody fuss about nothing,' said the F/H/B, fixing the lady with a straight stare. 'That happens yerabouts. Only on Exmoor 'tis t'other way round, the maids say it to the chaps.'

'Ooh, Mr Huxtable, you are a tease!' trilled our travelled lady. 'You can call it what you like, my dear,' he answered. 'But 'tis a fact of life yerabouts and neither you, nor the Hitalians nor anybody else is likely to change it.' And he leaned back against the door-post with the air of a man who has had his say and is well satisfied. As he might be, as this and like bits of homely information lead to many a lively discussion. However, I feel this might not have been said, solely for the ensuing debate it provoked on Exmoor.

Going one better over the Italians and our Common Market partners could well have had some bearing on the subject. The F/H/B views his continental contemporary with deep suspicion, labelling him as a scented, slippery customer who sweeps across his farmyard in a black, satin-lined opera cloak and patent shoes, leaping gracefully on to the dung heap to render a few bars from *Pagliacci*, only to take off after any female, from nineteen to ninety, who happens to be passing at the time. Not wholesome. And not to be trusted. The sort that blows kisses and gives his woman a bunch of flowers on her birthday instead of a load of logs for the solid fuel cooker. Impractical. And never make proper farmers. Something like that Frenchman we had turn up.

It would have to happen on a Saturday, the busiest day of the week. I was upstairs frantically changing the bed linen, when I heard the telephone shrilling in the kitchen, about a quarter of a mile away. Well, perhaps not quite, but it is a good distance, a fitness test, you might say. I flung myself down the back stairs and into the kitchen and grabbed the phone, to find that it was someone from the village calling to ask if they could bring five French farming people to see us, that afternoon. Certainly, I told them, but I would prefer Monday, thinking of all the Saturday arrivals and the tight Sunday schedule with the three meals. Not altogether suitable, said our village friend, as although four of the five visiting from France would be staying the week, poor Grandad had to leave for home on Monday.

I had a momentary vision of poor old Grandad being sent back to mind the farm whilst the rest of them cavorted on holiday. My decision was instant. 'Come right up,' I said. Within half an hour they were on the doorstep, two young couples accompanied by our friend from the village, but no sign of the old peasant farmer I was expecting dressed in his cords and leggings. The Grandad that stepped forward and bent his sleek, stylish head to kiss my hand and murmur 'Enchanted, Madame,' was tall, suave and dashing. No way was he my idea of a French farmer. Or any farmer, come to that. And without doubt, he was the best Grandad I had ever seen.

The F/H/B showed them all around the farm, the two young men being particularly interested as they were Grandad's sons and themselves farming in France. They all had a smattering of English, and our village friend knew enough French to hold the conversation together. The young wives were charming and they all seemed to enjoy our local offering of bread and cream and yeast cake. I fancied Grandad might just be more at home toying with beluga caviar. Before they left we found the reason he had to return to France on Monday was because he was booked to leave on a world cruise on Tuesday.

'Unbelievable,' I breathed.

'Daft as a brush,' muttered the F/H/B. 'Don't you try to tell me a proper farmer couldn't put that sort of money to better use on 'ees farm.'

And he is right in a way – our own small way, that is. Farmers in the South West with their small hill farms never allow themselves the luxury of even thinking of world cruises or anything else they might spend on like frivolities. Every single penny they ever make – and it is more often pennies than pounds – is ploughed right back into their farm, either in live or dead stock. And certainly not into the house where it rates as dead money. When farms are advertised for sale the house is scarcely mentioned, the acreage and quality of the land being what counts, and here the auctioneers may wax as lyrical as they please. For example, *'80-acre farm with good hedge and five-acre wood in fine hunting country. Four bullock sheds, shippon for twelve cows, implement shed, hay barn, fully renovated stables with range of loose boxes and new tack room. Modernised four-bedroomed farmhouse.'*

As the house is thrown in with the farm it obviously does not merit much advertising space, with the outbuildings and stables getting prime attention. Stables, in particular, rate very high in this particular area. Almost every able-bodied man, woman and child owns a horse. It is not regarded as a luxury as town-people might look on keeping such an animal, but as a necessity, part and parcel of Exmoor life.

Visitors to the moor are constantly surprised at the luxury horses enjoy compared to the spartan existence of most of their owners. Once, two of our guests were taking a moorland walk when they heard a bang and a crash and a clapped-out old Ford Granada pulled into a clearing just ahead of them. The driver's door was completely missing from the old wreck and there, seated in all his splendour, was an immaculately turned out gentleman, dressed in full riding kit, with polished black boots and a bowler hat which he politely raised to the surprised onlookers. Releasing his seat belt, he slid out of the doorless Granada and walked round to the horse box he was towing, letting down the tail-board to release a handsome chestnut thoroughbred. He mounted the horse, set his bowler at exactly the right slant, and cantered away across the moors, leaving the old Ford wide open to all the elements.

Now this, and like incidents, are quite acceptable and even common on Exmoor, but no doubt appear strange and possibly eccentric, to visiting folk's eyes. Here, material possessions such as high-powered cars and elegant furnishings count for little compared to the wild beauty of our surroundings and the freedom to do as we will, but it is often a difficult thing to explain to visitors who are used to a more urban existence. They puzzle, and even worry in their kindly way, that our transport is an ancient, unreliable pig van which begrudges us every mile, whilst in the stables are three horses, eating their heads off. Three horses, they reason, must surely equal one good car.

One of the first to voice this suggestion was Fred, a wizard with figures who spent many a holiday here, and who fairly gobbled up the motorway miles between us and his sub-post office near London, in his 2.5litre Rover. The F/H/B was totally taken aback at the indecency of the suggestion. He took off his cap and scratched his head, but it was not an answer that required a great deal of thought.

'What the hell would us do wi' a new car?' he finally asked. "Tis a luxury us can't afford, and you can't odds it.'

'But you've got three horses you could sell,' pursued the mathematical Fred.

'Sell? What be talking about, they live yer, same as us.' And he signified the conversation closed by ramming his cap back on his head and turning for the yard. The usually intrepid Fred, realising he was touching on a sensitive subject, never again suggested selling the horses.

Perhaps Fred would have got an insight into a countryman's mind had he been with us at a certain farm sale. The old bachelor farmer had died at eighty-seven and his farm, together with the livestock and machinery, was up for auction. This was advertised in the local press, and under a smaller headline came 'Household furnishings', which was why I was there, being interested in some cream pans which these days are virtually obsolete.

There was a long driveway into the farm, stopping at the buildings and leaving one field to be crossed on foot. The farmhouse had a sad, neglected look, but then they often do. I stepped inside through the back door into a little stone passage with the scullery and kitchen opening off. It was infinitely worse than the outside, and milling with people inspecting the various lots for sale. The sink in the scullery was a long, yellowish, drinking trough, over which was one cold-water tap, set in a line of old broken and cracked white tiles. An old mangle (Lot 17) stood against the wall and on a small table were bits and pieces of crockery alongside the cream pans, which looked as though they had not seen the light of day for many a year. I took down the lot number and resolved to make a bid.

Then I stepped through into the kitchen where the stone floor was partially covered with old pieces of frayed coconut matting and the paintwork was that gloomy brown so beloved by Victorians. Ancient bits of rag that had once served as curtains hung at the windows, whilst beside the open fireplace with its great iron kettle suspended on its handy-maid (a sort of iron string that makes tipping easy) was the armchair that the old man used to sit in. At some time it had lost its seat and the hollow was stuffed with a fleece of sheep's wool. However, it was nicely positioned opposite one of the best hunting pictures I have ever seen. It was a large wooden framed picture depicting a burly huntsman in his scarlet jacket, standing aloft on a vault in a churchyard holding at arm's length a dead fox, with the pack of hounds leaping up at it. So fascinating was it that there and then I made up my mind to forego the cream pans and possibly even next week's groceries, and splurge my all on that picture. And yet – would it not always remind me of that poor old man living and dying in squalor, with only his picture for company?

Turning, I almost collided with the F/H/B, so engrossed was I in my racing thoughts. Pointing at the picture, I asked, 'How do 'ee fancy that hanging half-way down our stairs?' He studied it closely.

'I seen better. Bit ghoulish, ain't 'ee?' he answered doubtfully. Then brightening, 'You come alonga me, a minute. You'll never believe your eyes not after this,' and he encompassed the dingy room with a sweep of his arm.

I followed him out the back door and across the small field to the outbuildings we had skirted on the way in. We went through a five-bar gate into a rough little yard with the usual old stone buildings, a hay shed, bullock house and a couple of calf pens. The F/H/B walked on to the top end where some old buildings had obviously been pulled down and replaced with a modern stable block. There, peering out of three of the most immaculate loose boxes I have ever seen, were three beautiful thoroughbreds, coats polished like satin, manes and tails trimmed, and each with its name carved in oak bark over the door. Inside, the stables were tiled from floor to ceiling, the wooden doors creosoted and the tack room on the end smelled wholesomely of saddle soap. Assorted pairs of riding boots stood in a neat line along one wall, there were bright curtains at the window, a Calor gas ring and a leather armchair.

'I don't believe it!' I exclaimed. 'I just don't believe it. How could he let his house go like that – not ever a proper armchair...'

'Lived for 'ees hosses,' the F/H/B explained. 'And lived with 'em, most the time. Chap that worked yer told me 'ees boss hardly missed a race meeting. Had a rare ol' life, 'ee did. 'Ope I'm enjoying mesel' 'alf as much when me time comes.' 'That settles it,' I said. 'That picture's as good as ours.'

We walked back to the farmhouse where the auctioneer had just got started and was obviously finding it heavy going trying to raise a few pence for the pathetic bits and pieces that passed as furnishings. The cream pans made their money and I felt a pang of guilt as I let them go without a bid, having been brought up to believe that thrift triumphs over all, whilst fixing my eye on a mere ornament like a picture could scarcely be termed thrifty.

I edged into the kitchen and took up my position to bid for the picture. To my surprise, there was only one other interested bidder besides myself, and in seconds the picture was mine for a mere five pounds. It seemed very little for such a picture auctioned in a hunting community, and I remarked so to the F/H/B.

'Well, 'tis like I telled 'ee,' he answered. 'Bloody ghoulish, that huntsman stood on somebody's tombstone waving a dead fox. Folks wouldn't hav'n in their homes. Can't understand you, Maid, come to that, not wanting thicky ole thing.'

I carefully loaded my picture in the pig van and bore it triumphantly home. It hangs now over the stairs, and often, when passing, I like to think of the old man gazing at it, in the short intervals that he spent away from his beloved horses, from the depths of his old fleece-stuffed armchair. I shall always consider it a bargain, in spite of the remarks it elicits from the Die-hards, such as, 'That thing gives me the creeps,' to the more polite, '*What* an unusual painting,' from newcomers. Either way, nobody is likely to walk off with it.

Come to that, I warrant that nobody is likely to walk off with very much from any little hill farmhouse in this area. Furnishings range from the strictly functional to shabby gentility, the most prized possessions not being a colour television set, or video, but the stags' antlers that adorn the walls, along with old sepia photographs of Masters and Huntsmen of various packs, now long gone.

However, if the house and contents hit rock bottom in a farm inventory, at least the farmer's wife is regarded as an investment, placed pleasingly near to the top, inevitably after the beef cattle and sheep, but certainly comparable with the farm pony. If you want to buy trouble, then you get a used model, and a second-hand woman is considered just slightly more disastrous than a second-hand horse.

One of our old neighbours, a bachelor known as the Pig Expert, had decided views on women, though to my knowledge he had never kept a woman in his life. Nor a pig, come to that. But he always held the attention of lady visitors to the pub once he got started on his favourite theme of horses and women. 'There be only two breeds of women in the whole world,' he would bellow, his back to the bar, flinging his arms wide as though to encompass his statement. The visiting ladies, listening with rapt attention to the charismatic old character, would be unaware that his travelling experience of 'The whole of the world,' was limited to a one-day excursion to Aintree in 1975 to watch the Grand National.

'Jus' two breeds, and I'll tell 'ee exactly what they be.' And he would lower his voice conspiratorially to his small audience. 'Racehosses and H'Exmoor ponies, that's what they be. Now racehoss women' – with a knowing shake of the head – 'they be for chaps that can afford h'ornaments. And H'Exmoor pony women, now they be for working chaps, like us be.'

There would be a pause whilst the Pig Expert took a long reviver from his cider mug and collected himself to deliver the punchline, which was usually directed at any listening menfolk. 'And,' he would continue, 'Which h'ever you picks, be sure' – and here he put slow emphasis on every word –'be sure you looks at their teeth *and* fetlocks. Never forgit the points of yer hoss, a front like a duchess and a backside like a barmaid. Hexackly! Beggin' your pardon, Ma'am.' This last remark would be addressed respectfully to the landlord's wife, a dignified lady drying glasses behind the bar.

By this time the Pig Expert was warming to his theme and expounded still further.

'Fresh h'air and h'exercise, that's what they wants, git the sun on the fillies' backs. Never keep 'em locked up, costs too much in h'eats. And talking of feeding, do 'ee bear in mind that the bigger the frame, the more they feed. You won't do no better than a nice little H'Exmoor with a medium frame.'

Then, turning again to the landlord's wife with a glance of approval, 'A bit like yersel', Ma'am, if you don't mind me a-saying so.'

'Yes, I do mind,' snapped the dignified lady, aware that she spent every spare minute endeavouring to reshape her medium Exmoor frame to a racehorse one. 'Us don't want that sorta talk yer, so just you watch it,' and she flounced through to the more genteel customers in the lounge bar.

'Did I say ort?' enquired the aggrieved Pig Expert after the departing Medium Frame. Then with a sad shake of his head. 'Takes after 'er Dad, 'er do. Temper'ment all to 'ell. N'ort good hever comes outa bad-tempered stallion. Got to keep yer reins tight,' greeted this sad philosophy, then the Pig Expert visibly jerked himself together.

'Goddamnit!' he suddenly roared. 'Where's that danged woman got to? Hey, Missus!' addressing the back end of the Medium Frame landlady through the door of the lounge bar. 'Yer, Missus, 'ows about topping us up, us got to drink a toast.'

The landlady bustled through and busied herself with the refills, then the Pig Expert raised his cider mug in his favourite ritual, 'Drunk or huntin',' he bawled. 'Never happier.'

This invariably brought a cheer from one and all, and his cider mug would be refilled time and again before he eventually weaved his unsteady way home.

They say on Exmoor that you should always persevere with that which you know best, and drinking and hunting are without doubt the two things the Pig Expert had studied above all else. No matter how many pints are sunk the night before, he could be relied on to be up and working a the crack of dawn, before presenting himself, immaculate, at the 11am Meet. He managed very well without a wife, but realised he would be better off with one, just somebody to be there, answer the telephone, fill out endless forms, deal with the Men from the Ministry, generally entertain callers and get a hot dinner every day. Not forgetting lending a hand on the farm when called upon, the sort that can dock a sheep with one hand and roll a fag with the other. The fag would be for farmer, of course.

As we get a certain number of single, divorced and widowed ladies on farm holidays, it is often tempting to match-make with some of our available males. Howsoever, the general feeling was aptly expressed by the F/H/B who reckoned, 'There ain't a lot in this ol' love lark, 'tis all a matter of h'economics.' This resulted in lady holidaymakers hardly being worth the bother, when most of the local bachelors cautiously considered the merits of a costly night out with an unknown lady against a night in with the latest edition of South West Farmer. One of these was 'Seemingly', a presentable, middle-aged bachelor who still lived with his aged mother. He was christened William fifty-odd years ago, but for as long as I can remember has always been addressed as 'Seemingly' on account of his constant use of the word. He often dropped into our kitchen, and I had researched thoroughly into seeking a bride for him. I broached the subject of an introduction one day when we had a charming lady holidaymaker staying for a two-week holiday. His first question was, ''Ow long's 'er yer for?'

'A whole fortnight. You could take her out quite often.'

'Yer, and what 'appens then? 'Er be go,' his voice shot up an octave as the injustice of it all took grip. 'And me money be go, too!'

'All right, then. Take her out to dinner, just once or twice.'

'Whaffor? 'Er's stopping with you, seemingly, and you'm s'posed to be feeding 'er!'

'Look,' I said reasonably. 'Don't you ever feel you'd like to dine out with a lady?'

'No need,' came the ready answer. 'Mother's got food home!'

To which there was no possible answer, so I decided to cut the pre-liminaries and introduce Seemingly to the lady in question and let chemistry do the rest. Hopefully, all I had to do was to light the blue touch paper and then stand aside and watch the rockets take off. I whizzed along to the sitting-room where the plump and pleasant little lady was doing her lonely crossword, and told her, 'There's somebody in the kitchen wants to meet you.' I endeavoured to make my words sound slightly mysterious, a Royal command from a visitor with a Mission, to meet just this one, important lady. She was right behind me on the return journey and smiled encouragingly at Seemingly as I made the introductions, before fading into the back-ground to watch my rockets take off. Sadly, they never got off the launching pad, fizzling out at Seemingly's first words as he eyed the spruce little woman.

'Be you,' he asked cordially, 'after I?'

My guest who was just murmuring her how-d'y-does blushed scarlet. 'Oh, no Mr – er, certainly not, I didn't know...' She cut it short and beat a flustered retreat to the safety of the sitting room, leaving me to have a few words with our friend on handling women.

'You don't even TRY,' I told him grimly. 'The way you'm gwaine on, you'll end up wi' a housekeeper.' I was well aware this was the most inflammatory threat I could use.

'A HOUSEKEEPER!' breathed Seemingly, as though fearful that someone might overhear. 'Never! 'Tis sinful, that be.'

'Rubbish. Farmer Chugg gits on pretty well wi' 'ees housekeeper.' I said this with a certain amount of spite, still smarting from the embarrassment I had just suffered, and knowing full well of our friend's rivalry with Farmer Chugg.

'Her's only there for one thing,' said Seemingly, a satisfied smile spreading over his homely countenance.

'Yes, companionship.'

'Geed 'ome. 'Er's after Farmer's money. And now I'll tell 'ee summat,' this with a look over one shoulder to make sure Farmer Chugg was not creeping up behind. ''Er've got 'er 'ands on it, seem-ingly.' He ended on a note of triumph.

'What a lot of ol' rot you do talk!' And then curiosity getting the better of me, ''Ow d'ye tell 'er've got 'er 'ands to Farmer's money?'

''Cos I seen where 'er spended it.'

'Seen what?'

"Er've a just..." Seemingly paused and made a strangely delicate motion with both hands at cupping an imaginery bust line – "er've a just had 'er bosoms lifted!'

'Nonsense', I cried.   Then, inquisitiveness triumphing over common decency, "Ow can 'ee tell?'

'Never you mind, Maid. I don't always say ort, but I knows what's a-gwaine on. And I'll tell 'ee sommert else.' He was warming to his theme. 'You jus' go over Farmer Chugg's yard come midnight and shout FIRE and I'll guarantee both heads come out the same winder. That's housekeepers for 'ee, seemingly!' And he leaned back in his chair, head to one side, thumbs in his braces, daring me to deny it.

'You'm a poisonous old hound,' I said, pouring him a cup of tea. 'And you'll never git nobody, the way you'm carrying on.'

'Yes, I will, Maid,' replied Seemingly. "Cos you'll keep lookin' for me.' And he buttered a slice of yeast cake and chomped contentedly at it, leaving my head going round in circles like a harvest bug at the enormity of finding him a bride.

Nevertheless, before the harvest moon had waxed, I selected another lady that I considered suitable for an introduction to our friendly bachelor.   She was an extremely attractive little widow woman who had booked in with us for a fortnight's holiday. Mrs Morgan was bright and vivacious, a comely blonde with a ready smile, and I got the impression that even if marriage was not her goal, at least she would make a good test run for Seemingly.

This time the introduction went without a hitch, and if he had not exactly been to a charm school, at least he had the sense to hold his tongue long enough for the lady to decide she liked what she saw. Seemingly even doffed his pork-pie hat respectfully, saying, 'Pleased to meet you, Ma'am, I'm sure,' and they were off to a flying start. Sadly, in spite of several outings, it all came to nothing. Before she left for home at the end of her holiday, Mrs Morgan recounted her adventures to us over the usual tea in the kitchen. William, she told us, was a very, er, interesting man, presentable, too, togged up in his best clothes, and he had certainly taken her to some, well, different, places from those in town. Darts matches, mostly. 'Eventually he asked me up to his bedroom to see his collection of harness.' There was an agonisingly long pause whilst she slowly stirred her tea.

'Yer, yer, go on,' encouraged the Farmer/Husband/Boss.

'Well,' she continued gravely. 'I didn't really mind going upstairs with him...' she paused delicately.

'No, no, course not. Go on!'

'But it was more like a museum than a bedroom, what with harness everywhere and old pictures all over the walls, and stuffed birds in glass cases...' she broke off again.

'And it put you off?' I prompted her.

'Not exactly. But he was still carrying that damn shepherd's stick he takes everywhere. In fact, he never laid a hand on me, just hooked that stick round my neck.'

'And then? What then?'

'I couldn't stand that, like catching a sheep. So I made a run for it.'

'Out the door?'

'I couldn't get to the door without climbing over piled up harness, so I took a short cut across the bed.'

'Cor, bless me soul! Did 'ee git away?' The F/H/B was anxious to know.

'Not directly. He got me round the ankle with the stick and shouted 'Gotcha, me little lamb!' as though he was enjoying it. Then I managed to get unhooked, don't ask me how, and I made the door.'

I was overcome with remorse. 'Me dear,' I told her, 'I couldn't feel more sorry about 'ort. I never thought...' My words trailed off.

'Oh, don't *worry*,' said the self-possessed lady. 'It never exactly got out of hand. In fact,' she added thoughtfully, 'it wasn't altogether the stick and the piled up harness that really put me off.'

'What then?' I asked, feeling stupid for not knowing.

'It was his pork-pie hat. He never took it off. Not once.'

Whilst I digested this in silent sympathy, the F/H/B pushed his chair impatiently back and left the table.

'I dunno' what you wimmen got to be so bloody fussy about,' he growled as he rammed his cap on his head and took off for the yard. I caught the query in my companion's eye. 'Oh, no, never,' I said emphatically to the unspoken question. 'He never wears his hat, you know, upstairs.'

Chapter Four

Wrinkling my brow and sucking hard on my pen, I sat at the kitchen table, alternating between reading my advertisement on page 19 of *Daltons Weekly* and staring blankly at my renewal form.

I had already improved on my first, very basic insertion, with its minimal B&B & H&C, by paying a little extra so that it now read 'Farmhouse bed, breakfast and evening dinner, H&C in rooms, lovely views and food main consideration.' Even so, it was flagging somewhat, enquiries having dropped from five or six a week to three or four at the most. A little extra something seemed to be called for and I scanned the other three hundred-odd advertisements for inspiration. Apart from the Spring Interior mattresses, which I felt should be standard anyway, and lovely views (I had that already) and children welcome (I was liking them less and less), only two other words leapt out at me from no more than half a dozen advertisements on the entire page. A smile replaced my frown as I penned DOGS WELCOME on my renewal form. It had an agreeable ring to it, more homely than DOGS ACCEPTED (too grudging), or DOGS TAKEN (rather than lose the booking).

If I was slow in conceiving these two extra words for myself, blame it on countryfolk's attitudes to animals, which vary considerably from townspeople's. They take their dogs everywhere as a matter of course, and whilst we consider ours an essential part of farm life, they are often treated more like necessary employees than members of the family. Our dogs only leave the premises to work elsewhere, on off-land or on loan to a neighbour, whilst the bulk of the great British dog-loving public expect their animals to accompany them visiting friends, on picnics and outings, and even on holiday. Country people would never consider calling on friends and neighbours with their dog at heel, let alone carrying a lap-dog everywhere. When farmers say they do not carry passengers, they mean just that. All animals must pay for their keep, the collies and gun-dogs working at the big jobs, and the Jack Russells and Border Terriers tackling the little jobs, like ratting and rabbiting. Ours is a more human-to-animal relationship, whilst gentler folk tend to treat their animals as pets or even like little persons.

Howsoever, the DOGS WELCOME addition proved a winner, and business picked up accordingly. It did not bother me one whit if they were treated as pets or little persons, though, paradoxically, I did have one set of parents, who, at their four-year-old's insistence, treated her like a dog.

At first I smiled, thinking it was a childish whim that would soon pass as she settled down to life on the farm, but as the week went on it was apparent that little Gloria's holiday was to be spent crouched under our dining room table, making an occasional grab at the assorted ankles thereunder. She never sat on a chair or even had a plate of her own, and tit-bits were passed underneath from her parents' plates. Mother and Father were a delightful couple, too nice, I thought, and far too patient for the precocious Gloria.

Irritated at the child's behaviour, I finally asked the doting parents if she could not sit on her chair at the table at mealtimes. 'Oh, no,' said Mother, as though surprised at the stupidity of such a question. 'She thinks she's a dog.'

Plates and cups rocked as the tablecloth was wrenched aside from underneath and Gloria's face appeared for a second, poked her tongue out at Mother, and retreated.

'Good dog,' said Mother, patting at the disappearing head. I felt I might have dealt more firmly with the situation if the parents had not been such old friends of ours. They had been guests for many years before Gloria arrived, and it seemed ungracious and ungrateful to turn on their offspring. Serenity positively radiated from them; a charming couple with professional careers, and now Gloria to set the seal on their happiness. It was beginning to seem almost normal when they left the dining room leading their child on a leather dog leash but rumbles of displeasure were coming from the other guests.

'They're a pair of twits,' growled one man.

'If that kid belonged to me it'd be quick march up them stairs,' avowed another.

Meanwhile, still squatting in her kennel under the table, Gloria was finding the canine life had its drawbacks when the demure looking lady at the top of the table, forgetting that Gloria was not a dog, absent-mindedly (so she said afterwards), and none too gently, stuffed a bacon rind in her mouth. My turn came when small, clammy fingers wrapped round my ankle like maggots round a sheep's tail and I wrenched away and stamped, not too hard, but just enough. A scream of rage came from down under, but up top, as a composed landlady, I endeavoured to steer breakfast through its normal calm channels. I felt guilty disrupting the peace by causing the child to yell but hopefully after this things could only improve, so it was all smiles with, 'More toast, Mr Smitherman?' and 'Would you pass the prunes, Mrs Jarvis, and I'll take them out of your way.'

Down under, it was all drama with the child that thought it was a dog being dragged screaming to her chair, where she sat sullenly for the rest of the week. With a plate. And a knife and fork.

Nevertheless, it seems hard to snatch revenge on children for misdeeds that parents should have nipped in the bud long before. The same goes for dogs, a basic lack of discipline in the home making them unloveable elsewhere. I often think the two have much in common, particularly when they flick me smug, you-dare-not-touch-me glances as they delicately sniff, consider, and finally nibble at morsels of home-bred lamb or breast of chicken ('not leg, dear, Boysie/Mavis never touches dark meat'). Mavis could be cured with a wallop and all Boysie needs is a normal dog's life. It might be interesting to see what Boysie would get up to if he were plucked from Mummy's bosom and slung out into the farmyard to lead a more natural life. Which would tempt his twitching nostrils first, the pig-shit on the left or the cow-shit on the right? Or he might settle for a quick plunge in the horse trough with its floating layers of green slime, followed by a brisk roll in a few chicken feathers. After giving it a try-out Boysie could well decide to return to his home comforts and daily grooming, thinking that country life was not his scene.

After all, we once had a country born and bred sheepdog who made it quite clear that he hated the rural life in general and his own work in particular. He always seemed vaguely unhappy, as though thinking there must be more to life than eating from a communal dish, making his own straw bed in the stable, and rounding up sheep and bullocks. He was a border Collie and we bought him from a local shepherd at eight weeks old, to serve his apprenticeship under our old sheepdog, Skipper, who was nearing retirement. We named the puppy Tufter, and in the early months he quickly mastered his basic training to sit, lie, stay, and to heel, but after his prep. school, as it were, he never quite made it to the next grade. Perhaps it was because he never showed the slightest enthusiasm for his work, usually appearing too immaculate, too breezy and, worst of all, too cheeky for a working sheepdog. He would bark defiantly straight at the F/H/B if ordered to start work on something that did not quite suit his own plans at that particular moment, his personal routine taking in daily visits to neighbours and even three-mile trips to the village. He would grumble loudly and argue vociferously over his simple allotted tasks and at the first splash of rain he would make for shelter, picking his way delicately through the mud with immaculate white paws. He was completely uninterested in field work and when instructed to 'Git around' the sheep he would like as not, sit down, carefully and determinedly, with his back to his work, fastidiously picking at his toe-nails. Then, when old Skipper was detailed to demonstrate rounding-up to his apprentice, Tufter would charge after the old dog, tugging at his ears and tail, anything to distract him from work.

With the cows he would circle uninterestedly, like a harvest bug, before zooming off up the hill towards the village, returning at supper time to find his half-demented master still shouting that he might as well go to bed and sleep for a week as waste time keeping a dog on the dole.

When Tufter was eighteen months old, several of our guests, sensing he would soon be out of a job, offered him homes, and we chose the one we thought would suit him best, at Bognor Regis. There he would have a large garden to play in, the nearby beach to run on, and a new home situated in a residential area with plenty of human company. No cows, no sheep, no wide open spaces, and, best of all, no work.

Tutfer left Chilcott with his new owners, Mr and Mrs Andrews, one rainy Saturday morning in October. It was as though he sensed something was up and he behaved accordingly, refusing to get into their car, but we shoved and pushed his unyielding frame into the back seat, slamming the door before he did a wheel-about. As they drove away I could see his nose, pathetically pressed against the rear window. I was consumed with guilt, a traitorous friend, ruthlessly trading-in a loveable dog for a newer model. Already his place was booked for a new apprentice, and I reminded myself, but for Master Tufter's wilfulness, old Skipper should now be retiring instead of facing another eighteen months' hard labour. I sighed heavily at the injustice of it all as the old dog, who had been standing with us silently watching his failed replacement drive off to his new life, muzzled comfortingly against my hand.

Before long, reports on Tufter's progress started to filter through. At first it was not inspiring. His proud new owners suffered their first embarrassment with his debut on the beach at Bognor, when he mistook a man in a brown shirt and brown trousers, sitting on the sand quietly reading, for a tree trunk. On his second outing he knocked down a screaming infant and seized its ice-cream. The new owners hooked Tufter's new red lead to his new red collar and crept homewards, determined not to appear again in public until their protégé's hillbilly habits had been schooled out of him. None of us had given a thought that what passed for manners on Exmoor might be a bit too rough and ready for the more sophisticated seaside.

Tufter was quickly booked into dog training classes, where, with his basic grounding of obedience already learnt on the farm, they were able to smooth away the rough edges and prepare him for the urban life he so favoured. He threw himself into his classes with a zest unknown in his sheepdog days, and soon became the star of the show. He won rosettes and diplomas, and his delighted owners telephoned to tell us he had been selected to represent Bognor Regis in the area finals for the Best Behaved Dog. He won, and went on to the South-eastern finals, where he was runner-up to the champion and was photographed proudly wearing a gigantic blue rosette. His busy life extended to good works and fund raising for charity on sponsored walks. At Christmas he telephoned us, garrulous as ever, barking his greetings down the line. He even sent old Skipper a Christmas card picturing a tipsy-looking poodle sporting a paper hat and drinking from a champagne glass. Inside was the jaunty message 'See Ya Soon.'

This was indeed so, as, come spring, Tufter was brought back to the farm for a week's holiday. Brushed and gleaming, he bounded in excitedly, howling loudly, straight up to the old dog who was wearily stretched out on the flagstones after his day's work. 'Hi-ya, old boy,' he seemed to be saying, between frantic licks at his old friend's sleepy face. 'Still hard at it, then?'

He could hardly be relegated back to his former residence in the stable, now inhabited by the muddy new apprentice, nor did I think he would relish sharing the communal trough, but even as I wondered, a soft, fluffy quilt was laid on the kitchen flagstones for him to sleep on. 'A pink bedspread,' I shrieked disbelievingly. 'His blue one's in the wash,' explained Mrs Andrews, as she placed on the table a spotless blue china feed bowl and a shiny round oven-dish. 'For his ox-cheek casserole on a Wednesday.'

I think Tufter enjoyed his holiday; he seemed glad to see all his old friends, including the farm cats, although he hurriedly skirted the sheep and bullocks, doubtless not wishing to be reminded of his working days.

He had to leave for Bognor early on the following Saturday as he had a social engagement in the afternoon. He and his girlfriend were to attend a dogs' fancy dress party, dressed as a bride and groom. It stretched my imagination to the limit to picture him strutting along in a top hat and bow tie. A crowd of us gathered in the yard to wave goodbye, including the F/H/B, old Skipper, the cats and assorted chickens. We all watched as Tufter climbed importantly into the back seat of the Peugeot and the car pulled slowly up the hill with our friends waving from inside. Only Tufter never looked back. He was a loveable dog, I thought, suddenly missing him, and nobody could begrudge him his ambitions. He had never deliberately set out to be a trouble-maker, not like some dogs whose actions cause maximum embarrassment, almost as though they despise their owners. Never was this more evident than in the Red Setter episode.

Mr and Mrs Plumb and their dog were booked for a week in September. On the Saturday afternoon I heard their car pull into the yard, I quickly prepared a tea tray and ran to open the front door, when whoosh – a Red Setter with a large man on the end of a leash leapt through the garden gateway, passed me at the front door, and shot straight up the stairs. In their wake, taking little running steps, followed a small, neatly-dressed middle-aged woman, wearing a distraught expression, clasping her hands together and murmuring 'Terrible, terrible,' in a little thin, high voice. I learned later that Mrs Plumb's vocabulary was limited to like utterances, all directed at the dog.

As my new guests were already assembled, panting on the upstairs landing, it seemed sensible to show them to their room. I opened the door to the Pink room and the Red Setter bounded in with a deep 'Woof' that could have stood for Geronimo, dragging his owner, a good 15-stoner, after him, seizing in his teeth en route my best sheepskin rug. Growling fiercely and shaking it from side to side, he leapt onto the four-poster bed, with Mr Plumb sprawling half-on and half-off, still valiantly clinging to the lead with both hands, and the little wife in the doorway breathing, 'Terrible, terrible.' Marching round the bed, I delivered a smarting one-handed clip to the dog's nose, grabbing the sheepskin rug with my other hand as he opened his jaws to yelp with pain and surprise, before sliding backwards on to the floor.

Mr Plumb also slithered off the bed, looking exhausted and dishevelled, and spoke breathlessly. 'Oh er, Mrs, er Huxtable, perhaps you should take the rug away. Er, yes, that's it, completely away. And anything else that's likely to, er, well, you know how these dogs are, you, er, have dogs of your own, I take it?' It was tempting to say, 'Yes, but not on beds,' but mindful that the customer is never wrong, I changed the subject. 'I expect you'd like some tea,' I offered. Mr Plumb seemed unwilling to move, possibly consolidating his position before the next mad gallop started. 'Er, yes, yes, most certainly, but we shall have to bring Justin with us, we daren't leave the old chap alone. You do understand, Mrs, er, Huxtable?' He turned to his wife. 'Help me tie him to the bedpost, dear, then I'll go to the car and get his toys and we'll have Mrs, er, Huxtable's nice cup of tea.'

I collected a few odd ornaments and a couple of cushions and stashed them with the rug out of Justin's reach. I passed Mr Plumb on the stairs carrying a large cardboard box bulging with rag dolls, chewed teddy bears and rubber squeakers. A whole week of Justin and his humourless owners was looming ahead and on the present showing it hardly seemed likely we would be staggering to bed every night holding our sides with laughing.

As it happened, had we so wished, we could have been in bed by 8.30 every night. Justin and Mr and Mrs Plumb were. After dinner all three went to bed; there seemed little else they could do. Walkies with the dog were obviously a nightmare, they dare not leave him in their car and he had given the sitting-room a going-over on his first night, finding the legs of the chairs more palatable than any of his toys that littered the carpet.

Mornings, before breakfast, Justin bounded up the road on what I suspected was his only exercise of the day, with his master clutching the lead and bouncing along behind, followed by the desperate little Mrs Plumb, wringing her hands and mouthing, 'Terrible, terrible.'

He was brought into the dining room at meal times and tied to the leg of the table with his favourite toy of the day to bite at. It was usually a squeaker, which did nothing for our nerves. After breakfast they settled him in the back seat of their car and drove him round the moors all day. Even so, there was something about that dog that was not unlikeable. Perhaps it was a slightly droll look in the way he rolled his eyes. There was a certain intelligence about him, as though he had sized up his inadequate owners and was knowingly playing them along out of devilment.

The F/H/B noticed Justin's possibilities and suggested to the Plumbs one morning that they might like to leave him behind for the day. 'I'll square'n up a bit for 'ee,' he obligingly offered. 'Then be the time you gits back tonight I'll have'n stood at the front door saluting as you comes in.' There was a horrified silence, then Mr Plumb methodically unwound the leash from the table leg. 'There is no call for that sort of treatment, Mr, er, Huxtable,' he said stiffly. 'Not with my dog.'

The conversation was closed, with Justin released from his tethering, taking a flying leap through the dining-room door, with Mr Plumb, like an inflated windsock, clinging on grimly. Mrs Plumb followed, her hands clasped tightly together, as though in prayer for the F/H/B. 'Cruel, cruel,' she avowed, hurriedly distancing herself from that unfeeling countryman, who, thumbs in braces, watched the departing trio with disbelieving shakes of his head.

That evening, as though in retribution, the Red Setter delivered his pièce de résistance. It was about six o'clock and I was entertaining Seemingly to tea, the F/H/B having earlier ridden off on the pony shepherding, when we heard a commotion in the yard. Hens were clucking, Clarence the cockerel was crowing, and through the kitchen window I could see the odd feather drifting across in the breeze. Not a soul was in sight. Nevertheless, it seemed wise to check and we both made for our boots with one accord. Standing in the yard, to my surprise, were the Plumbs. But not together. Mrs Plumb was in the corner by the cow-shed, quietly distressed, and across by the chicken house stood a white-faced Mr Plumb, with his dog, both hands clutching at the lead. Justin wagged his tail when he saw me and I thought in different circumstances we might well have been buddies. 'Is anything wrong, Mr Plumb?' I enquired, concerned that he looked so pale and ill.

'Indeed there is, Mrs, er, Huxtable. Yes, yes, indeed there is. It took considerable effort for him to answer. It was a beautiful evening. The clucking and crowing had ceased, everything appeared orderly, yet there was an air of tension overall that I had come to associate with the Plumbs. It was lost on Seemingly who scraped his boots impatiently, wanting to get back to his tea.

Mr Plumb made a visible effort to collect himself, cleared his throat, and commenced.

'My wife's dog,' he said, disclaiming ownership, and meticulously pronouncing every syllable 'has just killed one of your chickens.'

There was a little moan from the corner by the cow-shed as Mrs Plumb re-lived the horror. Oh, Justin, I thought, you are wicked to upset them like this. I sympathized with his master, struggling with his confession.

'My wife,' he went on, 'took the dog's lead, only for a minute, you understand, but she couldn't hold him. He's such a strong dog, it takes a man to handle him.' Beads of perspiration dotted his forehead. 'He was across that yard and seized the little hen before – before...' His voice trailed off miserably.

'Where be 'er to, then?' Seemingly wanted to know practically. He had a point. The yard, normally teeming with ducks and hens and guinea fowl, seemed deserted. Even Clarence, the resident cockerel, had vanished.

Mr Plumb still stood his ground, his knuckles turning as white as his face with the effort of gripping the dog's lead with both hands. I noticed a feather twitching gently in the corner of Justin's mouth. His master gathered himself together.

'Before I take you to the – the little dead hen, Mrs, er, Huxtable, there is something I must add to, er, what I have told you.'

There was a strangled cry from the corner by the cow-shed as Mrs Plumb re-lived the slaughter yet again. 'Terrible, terrible!' she wailed.

I felt sudden alarm, looking round the deserted yard. 'He can't have killed the lot?' I wanted to know. 'No. Just the one. But the upsetting part was,' the pale cheeks quivered with emotion, 'the upsetting part was, as that little hen lay there dying, your Clarence came flying across from somewhere over there,' he indicated vaguely the direction of the dung heap, 'jumped on her little corpse, and – and had his wicked way with her.'

'My goodness,' I said faintly, feeling some remark was expected of me, and taking care to avoid Seemingly's eye. Mr Plumb looked a slightly better colour after his confession and still tightly gripping the dog's lead, led us round the tractor trailer. 'There,' he said, pointing dramatically down to a little flattened patch of grass. Our eyes followed his to a few straggly brown feathers moving gently in the light breeze. A few yards away hopped a small, bedraggled hen, slightly dazed, but definitely a survivor.

'Is that your dead hen?' I asked Mr Plumb.

'Why, er, yes, yes, my word, I do believe it is,' he burbled.

Seemingly could contain himself no longer. 'Har, har, har,' he cackled. ''Er ain't daid at all. More like ol' Clarence gived 'er the kiss o' life.'

Still in the safety of her corner by the cow-shed, Mrs Plumb uttered a twitter of disapproval at the coarseness of farmyard life.

There was a clatter of hooves in the gateway as the F/H/B, back from his shepherding, trotted the pony into the yard.

'What's gwaine on, then?' he enquired, sensing drama as he slid from the saddle and we all stood motionless eyeing the recovery of the hen. Only Seemingly answered. 'Ol' Clarence bin at it again,' he grinned. 'But fer 'ee you'd be one hen less. Bleddy ol' dog pretty nigh killed 'er.'

'Mr Huxtable,' said Mr Plumb, obviously feeling Seemingly was taking matters a bit far in crediting Clarence with the chicken's recovery, but anxious for an honourable settlement.

'Mr, er, Huxtable,' repeated Mr Plumb. 'My wife had, er, a slight accident with her dog. It was, er, unfortunate, most unfortunate, that one of your little hens was injured, and had the outcome been less happy…' He broke off to eye the semi-naked chicken, which was still bemusedly hopping round in little circles. 'Had the outcome been less happy,' he continued more firmly, 'I should have most certainly reimbursed you, Mr, er, Huxtable.'

''Ow much?' the F/H/B wanted to know, briskly unbuckling the girth strap.

'I beg your pardon?'

''Ow much. For the chicken,' pursued the F/H/B.

'Oh, indeed, yes. Well, it would have, er, been a mutual agreement, of course, and well, it has actually happened once before. With a neighbour's bird. We settled for, er, £8.'

'Eight quid? For a chicken?' The F/H/B was incredulous. 'You can take the lot at that price. Fact is,' he concluded, slipping a halter over the pony's head, 'none o' this woulda happened if you'd done like I said and left that bleddy dog behind this morning.'

I could see that although Mr Plumb was not disposed to carry on the conversation, he was as yet reluctant to stir the now subdued Justin, who was stretched out straight as a gun barrel with his handsome red head resting on his paws. He made a decision.

'Over here, my dear,' he called to the little wife, still in her corner and plainly fearful that a single step forward might provoke another disaster. However, she obediently tripped across, giving the pony and the F/H/B a wide berth.

'We shall handle him together,' said her husband firmly. 'Now then, your two hands on the lead, and mine just above.'

As Mr and Mrs Plumb planned their trip across the yard I noticed the dog's eyes roll a little and his fine frame tense. He knew what was expected of him and would make sure they were not disappointed. As his owners straightened, Justin leapt into life, charging across the yard at his usual crazy gallop, with the two of them bouncing unhappily along in his wake. He must have been towing well over 20 stone.

Seemingly, for once, was almost dumb-struck. 'Well, I'm buggered,' was all he could manage.

'Me, too,' said the F/H/B plaintively. 'Eight quid for one bleddy chicken. Us only paid 50p for ten in the fust place. Why you lot got to interfere I'll never know.'

I picked up the chicken, who still appeared somewhat disorientated after her frightening experience, and carried her to an empty calf's house which we often use as a sick-bay. By the end of the week, apart from a couple of bald patches, she had completely recovered.

Justin left on the Saturday, much as he had arrived, with a leap and a bound through the garden gate. Nobody expected the over-burdened Mr and Mrs Plumb to leave a bottle of whisky with a jolly little thank-you note tied to the cork, so we were not disappointed. We had a month's grace before the next dogs arrived, in mid-October. All 35 of them. Or $17^1/_2$ couple, if their huntsman were counting them, hounds always being accounted for in couples.

Earlier in the year we had been selected to entertain a visiting pack of foxhounds on a hunting weekend from Yorkshire. The Master and Huntsman and followers of the Pennine Foxhounds were to be accommodated in the house, and the F/H/B volunteered to kennel the pack in one of our farm buildings. Hunting folk are notorious timekeepers, so I half expected them to arrive late for dinner on the Friday, although they were booked for dinner at 7.30. It was a rough Autumn night, with hard, slanting rain, and the hound box eventually rattled into the yard just after 3am, after what must have been a nightmare journey of over 300 miles. The hounds were let out of their lorry and followed their huntsman across the yard to the shed where the F/H/B had laid out their food in troughs. They hungrily attacked it, but as soon as the huntsman left and pulled the sliding door on them, they charged after him, knocking the door outwards and escaping underneath, then howling in full cry across the yard. Three times the weary huntsman shut them in, and three times they howled their way back across the yard, until he finally 'Gave them best,' as he called it, by making himself a straw bed and settling down with them for what was left of the night.

At 7.30 the hunters were all booted and spurred and eager to commence hunting down through our valley. We had permission for this from the Masters of the Dulverton East Foxhounds, for although the land belongs to us, the hunting rights are accepted as Dulverton East 'country', every pack in the land having its own area and etiquette demanding that masters be consulted before any visiting hounds hunt their particular 'country'.

The charming Master of the Pennines thought they might be a little late for breakfast, but in no way did he wish to inconvenience us. Perhaps half an hour? It was still raining hard and they would not expect to stay out long in such weather. 9.30 was agreed on, so I mentally registered 10.30, give or take an hour. They arrived back for breakfast at 2.45, drenched and starving. Their scarlet coats were so weighted with rainwater I would have needed a winch and pulley to haul them up to the bacon hooks in the kitchen ceiling to drip-dry, but the hefty huntsmen hoisted them up and rivers cascaded from the jackets and flowed across the flagstones, pooling up by the doors. Their boots were full and their hats were sodden and we lined them up on the rack over the Rayburn where they dripped with brisk spats on to the hotplate below.

The 10.30 breakfasts had long since been consigned to the pig bucket, so I prepared fresh jumbo-sized ones and gallons of scalding hot tea which I noticed they were generously topping up with whisky. Purely medicinal, they assured me, to combat wet and cold.

That evening, with the hounds securely nailed in their quarters, we took their masters off to the local pub where the local foxhounds had arranged a social evening in their honour, including a skittles match, refreshments and a sing-along. The beer flowed, the skittles tumbled, horns blew 'Gone Away', and in the sing-along our visitors greatly impressed with their baritones, tenors and yodellers and songs that ranged from the mournful ('Death of Old Shep') to the rousing ('John Peel'). Such talented soloists with their broad, honest faces shining with effort and enthusiasm, were as good as a two-fingered salute to our own musical inadequacies, as we could do little more than join in their choruses. That is, until just before the close at midnight when one of our own hunt ladies stepped forward, amidst respectful applause, to represent the West Country with our only solo of the evening.

She was a tall, handsome woman, square-shouldered and almost haughty in appearance. Dressed in a sensible jumper and skirt and woollen stockings she was a sharp contrast to the imposing figure I remembered astride her lively chestnut, with her bowler hat and black jacket complementing her fair skin and her blondish hair gathered severely in a fine hair net.

Hands clasped before her, she commenced to sing, her beautiful, controlled soprano voice soaring heavenwards, like a divine soloist from the church choir at evensong. Hunting horns were stilled as the clear, high voice took over, although anyone expecting to leave the sing-along on a spiritual note would have been disappointed. It was not a sacred song. It was not even a hunting song. It was not jazz, pop or blues. It was pure, unadulterated rugby ribaldry, with unbelievable words, ending in a lewd chorus of rub-a-dub-dub, rub-a-dub-dub, which, after the initial shock, everybody joined in delightedly. Indeed, such was the enthusiasm for the lady soloist that several huntsmen seized and heaved her on to a skittle table, still singing, to complete her finale in a storm of applause and encores.

The Master of the Pennines, wiping away tears of mirth, stepped from the crowd to personally assist the singer down from her platform on the table, then turned to me saying it had been such a grand night, was it not a little early for it to close? He had no wish to inconvenience us, but perhaps some of the ladies and gentlemen from our own hunt might like to accompany us home, and we would round off the night with a few more songs.

Back home, about 40 of us packed into the sitting room and the singing reached a crescendo. At 3am I made tea and sandwiches, at 4am, the non-residents, growing hoarse, made a move for home, but the Pennines, still in fine voice, sang them off the premises. By 4.30 the Master was calling for a corkscrew to open a bottle of sloe gin. 'We'll sup to a great night, lass,' he toasted, slopping generous measures into glasses. 'Just hope we haven't inconvenienced you good folk, that's all.'

Sunday morning dawned almost before we hit our beds, but a couple of hours worked wonders for us and long before breakfast the visiting Huntsman let his hounds out in the yard for exercise. Unfortunately, somebody had left the back door open, and when I returned from stoking the sitting-room fire it was to find four or five shaggy great fell-hounds milling round the kitchen. The breakfast sausages (4lbs) and bacon (3lbs) had vanished, along with the paper they were wrapped in. The door to the dairy was open and with sudden fear I rushed through. It was justified. The pack in the dairy had scored heavily over the kitchen hounds, with a piece of ox-tongue, half a joint of boiled ham, a rib of roast beef and two loaves of sliced bread.

As I belted them out to join the others in the kitchen they spotted Jackson, one of the ginger cats, standing his ground in the window seat. The reinforcements were too much for the little cat and he took to his heels, as, with one accord, they leapt towards him. Through the dining room, up the front stairs, along the passage, down the back stairs and into the kitchen, Jackson running for his life and the hounds in full cry, thirsting for the cat's blood. He had reached the landing on his second trip round, when a lady Pennine, wondering at the commotion, opened her bedroom door and he thankfully shot in to safety under her bed. Grabbing a broom, I literally swept the hounds out of the house. They smashed the cat's dish on their way and one thought, unwisely, that he had time to shed his load before he made the back door.

We managed breakfast on our reserves, and it was music to my ears when I heard that final purp-purp as the hound lorry wound its way up the hill. They were all there, looking cheerily out through the slatted sides with their sterns waving in happy salutes. I waved back, telling myself resolutely that not every landlady has the honour of entertaining a visiting hunt.

Now, when visitors write describing their dogs, I know exactly what they mean:

Highly strung: Will tear the place to pieces.

Friendly: Slobbers over everybody.

Wonderful house dog: Howls all night.

Nervous: Can't wait to get out and pee all down the stairs.

Endearing: Does BIGS in strange houses but gets nearer the door every day.

Boisterous: Over-sexed and chases the cats with amorous intentions.

Eats anything: Gobbles all the scraps your own dog normally has.

Pack of Hounds: Gobble everything you normally have.

Chapter Five

There was a gentle tap on the kitchen door and a neat little lady who had spent many holidays with us entered. I looked up enquiringly from the lump of dough I was pummelling into bread rolls. 'You're after something, Mabel, I know it!' 'No said Mabel,' slightly hesitant. 'I just wondered if you knew about the trout.' 'Trout? What trout?'

'The one in the lavatory cistern upstairs. The top's off and there's this trout floating in the water and a notice pinned on the wall that says Live Trout For Sale, Small Size Flush Once, Large Size Flush Twice.' Fred, I thought, it's got to be Fred. Dear, laughable, predictable Fred, our mathematical genius, was back for another holiday and up to his tricks again. Come rain, come shine, Fred went on forever. Nothing ever daunted him and he had arrived with his wife Doris that day and sensed an atmosphere that was fretful, to put it mildly.

It was June, a cold, wet and windy June, and the visitors were huddled round the log fire in the sitting-room listening to the T.V. newscaster announce that Midsummer's Day was officially colder and wetter than the previous Christmas day. Furthermore, most of the guests in this depressing week were in themselves depressed in one way or another. There was Geraldine, a deserted wife who had holidayed with us since she was a child, now with her own children, spoilt and unbearable. Her sad little tale was recounted over and over about the husband who had run off with the girl from the pet food shop where he bought ants eggs for their goldfish. She kept crying bitterly, despite all our attempts to comfort her. 'He even took the goldfish,' she sobbed broken-heartedly.

Another old guest that week was formerly a very jolly lady who seemed to have developed a severe nervous complaint, existing on 29 pills a day, including Valium, mooning unsteadily and moodily around as though constantly cidered up and snapping at her long-suffering husband.

Mabel, who had told me about the trout, had problems of her own, her husband having announced on arrival that he was taking to his bed and would get up when it stopped raining. He was a man of his word, arriving on Saturday and staying in bed until Tuesday, sleeping, reading, eating and saving petrol. He had morning tea at 8am, a full breakfast at 9am, beef tea at 11am (at his own insistence), lunch at 1pm, afternoon tea at 4pm, dinner at 7.30 and cocoa 'made with fresh, not skimmed milk' at 10.30. Mabel would willingly have waited on her suffering husband to save me the trouble, but obviously had orders to explain to me that, 'He wants to see someone different, he says he gets tired of seeing me all the time.' I silently hoped seeing that trout in the cistern would give our invalid a big enough shock to shoot him out of the house in his night-shirt never to return.

Fred's idea of the floating fish, if exaggerated, was not as unlikely as it appeared to be with Fred knowing our water system almost as well as the F/H/B. He had seen me many a time after torrential rain yanking at the kitchen tap, very nearly performing my own little rain dance of total disbelief at the meagre dribble that trickled out. Then I would stick a finger as far as I could reach up the tap and tickle around a bit in the hope that it connected with whatever obstruction was likely to be there. A hefty tug and a whoosh of muddy water signified success, with a little knotted bundle catapulting into the sink for identification. It often turned out to be curled-up worms, or a 12-inch string of slime, a fat little frog, or, if it had fur and a tail, a member (late) of a mouse family.

This was not a task for the squeamish, and Fred was one of the few that knew of these secret rituals at the kitchen sink. So he would sit quietly and loyally at dinner with other guests as the water jug was passed round and the diners exclaimed at the softness and crystal clarity of Chilcott spring water. 'You should bottle this and sell it,' they used to say, and, indeed, some even filled containers to take home, although I never recall anybody offering to pay for it.

Townsfolk always seem to think there's something romantic about spring water from a private supply, but that's before they spot the dead sheep upstream, or cotton on that the local kids don't chant nursery rhymes so much as meaningful ditties like, 'When the weather's warm and dank, you can sniff the septic tank.' Worse still is when the weather is cold and dank and blowing and raining and you've got to take to the hills to search out your romantic moorland spring, armed with a shovel, a pint pot and a stop-watch. The shovel is for general use, the pint pot is to catch the in-flow, and the stop-watch to time one pint. Which is all very well if you're a bit of a scholar and can do your multiplication tables well enough to estimate exactly how many gallons per hour are flowing in – or out, if you're unlucky, and it's all oozing out somewhere under your welly boots. From now on it's togetherness time for you and your shovel.

Private springs are very individual and owners learn about them by trial and error, soon catching on that they might as well blow their money on a good night out as send for a plumber who deals only with household pipes. Nevertheless, many a countryman, even nowadays, would still prefer to pump their water from a well, insisting on its purity even as they skim a shovelful of drowned mice off its surface.

Private water supplies tend to be like stocks and shares, either boom or bust. Just as everything is ticking along nicely, two weeks dry weather hits the South West, along with the first sign of recession when the lavatory cistern loses its potential and pensions itself off, with a last dying gurgle at the end of a negative day.

From then on it's downhill all the way, consignments of water being imported to share amongst neighbours, carefully measured drinks, and never forgetting the livestock take priority over the humans. That has never changed throughout the years but mercifully progress has taken over from just one tap inside the back door of a farmhouse to proper sinks and even bathrooms upstairs. Bathrooms were considered unnecessary with one farmer I know claiming he hadn't had a bath for sixty years, 'And I'm liy white!' whilst old Farmer Booper declared, "Tain't natural for water to travel hupwards!'

The worst thing that can happen to water supplies is the pipes jamming up with air. This usually happens after some small disaster and the water-flow is interrupted, or broken. We used to have some pipes lying above ground – I suppose because nobody had ever bothered to cover them in – and I recall our old sow, Minnie, vandalising one of the joints and wallowing in the resultant swimming bath with her dozen piglets as water gushed unchecked over the delighted family. The F/H/B re-connected the pipes but next day saw a repeat performance. And the following day. They wallowed in it whilst back at the homestead we spent three days on the trot without water. On the fourth day, and thereafter, Minnie and her family were locked up, whilst we did battle indoors with the air-locked pipes which banged and squealed like the little piglets had washed up inside and were yammering to get out. The F/H/B yelled, 'Work the taps, Maid,' a bit like a ship's captain commanding, 'all hands to the pumps, men!' as I raced upstairs and down, twisting every tap I could find on and off to spasmodic spurts of water until at last there was one final terrifying screech and a great whoosh of muddy slurry gushed out of the taps. Nobody minded the colour, people could wash again, bath even, and a mother tell her children, 'Run to the toilet, dear,' instead of 'Stop making such a fuss, just get down behind that gorse bush.'

Every now and again, an official from the Water Board collects a sample from private springs for analysis, which is quite comforting because it shows officialdom actually cares about what we flush down our innards. Last year, after the sample was taken, the man from the Board telephoned to enquire after our health and to warn us the sample was contaminated. He was very nice about it, reflecting that no doubt our insides might be accustomed to such impurities but he feared for his own after drinking a cup of tea with us. The F/H/B steamed away up the hill to investigate the spring and there on the moorland stood the cause of our problem. Three stray horses had taken shelter from the bad weather in that particular spot and were tidily grouped with their backsides suspended over our reservoir, doing what comes natural. A fence had to be hastily erected to keep out the marauders and the next water test was as pure as water usually is without, well, additives.

I assume these tests are undertaken in laboratories, but I wouldn't mind betting there're still some old stagers about that can roll a noggin' of Adam's ale round their gums and tell the difference between the bouquet of a dead sheep upstream or a few horse droppings down-stream. And, similarly, trout aren't quite the thing to have in your lavatory cistern, although everybody appreciated Fred's joke without realising all the implications. It went some way towards brightening up what threatened to be a dismal little gathering – excluding Fred, that is, and the bright-and-breezy Doris. I despatched Fred to remove his trout before the joke and the fish got stale, and he brought it to the kitchen, laying it carefully on a plate. 'Is it fresh?' I asked dubiously, thinking of the cat's supper. 'Fresh?' choked Fred, outraged. 'He's so fresh his eyes is still twinkling.'

◇◆◇

It looked like uphill work all the way for Fred and Doris that dismal wet week in June but there were still two more guests to come and I hoped they might be better company than the sad little bunch huddled round the sitting-room fire. It was not to be. Mrs Fogerty swept through the front door loudly announcing that she and her husband were Lord Mayor and Lady Mayoress of a well-known North Country town. She was a stout, middle-aged woman, carefully coiffeured, jangling bracelets, and domineering to the extent that her husband never referred to her by any more personal name than 'boss'. Mr Fogerty, whom she called Viv, was a complete contrast to his wife, a good looking, likeable man with wavy brown hair and twinkling blue eyes, but palpably fearful of upsetting his 'Boss'.

I felt the Fogertys were setting the seal on what was to be one of our less enjoyable weeks but our disappointment with one another was mutual. Mrs Fogerty trumpeted that she had acquired our address from the B.B.C. after hearing me talking about Exmoor and mentioning that I took summer visitors. She had therefore booked at a farm owned, she reasoned, by a B.B.C. personality and now made no attempt at concealing her disappointment that this was not so, balefully accusing, 'You talk just the way you did on Woman's Hour and I thought you were an intellectual putting on a funny voice!'

She was a vegetarian so was totally in alien territory as Exmoor prides itself on its fresh meat, and like most farmers we have always slaughtered our own pigs, lambs and poultry, with finest local beef supplied by the resident butcher. It was not altogether surprising that dinner times this particular week, turned out to be morbid little gatherings in stark contrast to our usual convivial sessions round the meal table. The deserted wife stared at her plate, whilst her two children noisily quarrelled opposite, the Valium lady sat square with her different coloured pills staked out in neat rows on the tablecloth, and Mr Valium hovered anxiously over his wife.

'Shall I fill your water glass, dear?' he would inquire, only to receive a querulous 'Yes – no – oh, I don't know, just don't keep asking me questions.' Kindly little Mabel looked sympathetic and willed the rain to stop in the hope that her husband might get out of bed and drive her out in the car, whilst Fred and Doris looked to be the only ones enjoying themselves, loving their food and laughing together. Viv, the Lady Mayoress' husband, would have obviously liked to join in with them, but dared not. Fred was already persona non grata with Mrs Fogerty for passing her the salt which she swept away with a regal wave of her hand and the words, 'The Queen does not take salt!'

If she tended to pick at her vegetarian dishes, her weakness lay in desserts, although she made it quite clear, even after a double helping, that they would need to be in a different class altogether to attain the perfection of the banquets she attended in her official capacity. Digging into her Baked Alaska, Mrs Fogerty wondered had I tried it with fresh peaches, it really did make a difference.

I protested that the dessert was made with loganberries because they were all I had as she tipped another spoonful of clotted cream over her Alaska, advising, 'Well, next time just you try fresh peaches, I'm sure you will find an improvement.' There was a murmur of dissension round the table, like a little mutiny brewing up, as the Lady Mayoress lowered the spoon she had been pointing in my direction, jangled her bracelets, and started with renewed vigour on her dessert. The others were all enjoying theirs and didn't give a pig's turd that they had never been to a mayoral banquet or even tasted peach Alaska and I could sense they were all 100 per cent on my side. Even Viv tipped me a nod and a wink which went some way to restoring my floundering confidence.

There was a respite from the rain on Tuesday morning which lasted long enough for Mr Gordon to leave his bed and take Mabel out for a drive. It thickened up again after lunch and the guests were glad to return to the sitting-room fire again, play scrabble and top up with tea and yeast cake. The weather was so bad that all were agreed that sunny summers seemed to be a thing of the past. The Lady Mayoress wondered idly what the weather was like in Barcelona. 'It was a toss-up, you know, between Spain and Exmoor and, well, Viv wanted the English countryside and he always gets his own way, don't you darling?' She spread her heavily-ringed hand expressively towards the rain-spattered window, sighing loudly. Back in the kitchen I snatched up the daily newspaper and scrabbled through the pages to find the world temperature chart. I was convinced the sun had not shone anywhere on earth for a very long time. There it was, Barcelona, sunny 85. I decided not to mention it.

On the dot of ten every night the Lady Mayoress would stir in her chair, look at her watch, and, raising her voice an octave, would shrill, 'Viv! I'll have my hot water NOW.' Viv, who never joined in cards or scrabble, preferring to quietly read, would snap shut his book, smile handsomely, and catapult from his chair like a good-looking greyhound from a trap, straight to the kitchen for a cup of hot water with a slice of lemon in it. Back in the sitting room he would hand it smilingly to his wife with a friendly little platitude. 'That's about the right temperature, my dear, just try it.'

'I'm not ready to try it,' she snapped once, irritably. 'Just put it on the table and leave it – no, not that table, this one here!'

One night when Viv came to the kitchen some of the neighbours were visiting and the whisky bottle was doing its round, so the F/H/B pushed a glass with a treble in it into his not unwilling hand. He downed it with the gusto of a man on a teetotal week's holiday with a wife whose idea of a nightcap was a cup of hot water. Viv obviously would have liked nothing better than to join the party, but duty called. 'Bugger it,' he said. 'I got to get back to Madam Kruschev.'

'How does he put up with her?' I marvelled to the F/H/B as we settled in bed that night.

'Easy,' he answered. 'He's got a bit on the side, he'd never stand her otherwise.'

'Well, why stop with her, then?' I wanted to know.

'Money,' said the F/H/B laconically. ''Tis simple. Money talks. And scandal. Don't forget he's the Lord Mayor, he wouldn't want that in the *News of the World*.'

I had forgotten. We had heard all about my Lady Mayoress but the Lord Mayor never merited a mention. I fell asleep listening to the rain and mouthing a little prayer for better weather.

My prayer went unanswered, and the next day, Thursday, was the worst day of the week, if not of the year. By mid-morning the house was clear, the visitors seeking a couple of hours of hopefully drier weather in Minehead, which, although only half an hour's drive away, enjoys a more temperate climate, whilst the F/H/B drove off to South Molton market to survey prices in that direction.

I cleaned the house and made cakes for the visitors' tea, and by mid-afternoon they were all back claiming their chairs by the fire and bewailing that Minehead for once had failed to live up to its reputation and was awash with overflowing gutters and grim- faced holidaycampers with plastic bags over their heads.

I stoked the fire with the last of the logs and dressed up in mac, boots and sou'wester, and pushed the wheelbarrow across the yard to re-stock from the heap in the circular-saw shed. I loaded as many as I could manoeuvre through the mud, heaved them off at the front gate, and was returning across the deserted yard for a second load when something struck me as odd. The F/H/B had loaned a stable to Tom, a near neighbour, to house a young horse he had bought to break in and sell on, hopefully at a fair profit, to offset some of the losses he had suffered after a run of bad luck. Tom turned up three times a day, twice to clean, groom and feed the horse, and once to lunge and back it. The rest of the time the lively little gelding spent hanging over his door and whinnying to anyone who passed. This day was unnaturally quiet, so I rested the wheel-barrow and peered into the stable to check that all was well. The little horse was lying down and appeared to be asleep, but didn't look up when I spoke to him, which was unusual, so I opened the door and went in for a closer look.

He was clearly unwell but I needed him on his feet to get a better idea of what was wrong. I positioned myself behind him and gathered all my strength to give his back-end an almighty heave, when I became aware of an ominous sounding click piercing the silence. It was regular. Click, click, click. I straightened and walked round to the horse's head, where the clicks sounded loudest. Blue sparks spat from the corner of his mouth and between his teeth was the electric light switch, torn from the wall and giving off the deadly clicks. His dark coat shone from Tom's daily brushing, he was well-fed and cared for but he was dead. I felt upset, stupid, befuddled, disbelieving but realised the power must be switched off from the mains in the house. And I had to break the news of the tragedy to Tom, who was already suffering a run of bad luck with his horses.

With most of the lights on indoors that dreary afternoon, I thought it best to warn the guests that there would be a power cut for a time, but on entering the sitting room I found an unexpected bonus. They were all asleep, slumped in armchairs with opened books and newspapers sliding off their laps, which saved me trumping up an excuse as it was essential they were uninformed of any tragedy on the premises. They were holidaymakers getting away from humdrum city lives and certainly not to be burdened with any of our problems. It seemed to work successfully, because one or another would often say, 'Oh, I wish we could live like you country folk, without any worries!'

After switching off at the mains I telephoned Tom to come over at once and he arrived in his Land-Rover at the same time as the F/H/B returning from market. Both wondered what they would have found had I touched the little black horse. We all cried over it together before securing the stable doors and I went in to make the visitors' tea and switch the lights on again. Tom and the F/H/B sloshed

Grouse into their tea while I found comfort in downing mine scalding hot, and we still cried a bit. The practical side had to be attended to and insurance policies were looked up, including one that covered livestock death from electrocution. Then the Hunt kennels were contacted to collect the horse the following morning, but not before 11am to ensure no guests would be there to see it. We all agreed that if anyone missed the lively, enquiring whinny, we would tell them Tom had taken the horse away.

Our neighbour left for home, dejected and sad, aware that the insurance company would settle for the value of his loss, but, like all countrymen mourning over a little horse's life, that was beyond a price ticket. The F/H/B wrapped up in waterproofs to collect the wheelbarrow with the logs that I had abandoned earlier, made up the visitors' fire and the kitchen Rayburn, and left for the fields to check the sheep and bullocks. With all the delays taking toll on my cooking time, I knew I would have to go full out to get the dinner on the table by 7.30. Two legs of lamb went into the oven, and it was when I rolled out the pastry for a gooseberry tart that I noticed small puffs of smoke coming from the Rayburn. The small puffs soon billowed into big puffs and little black smuts joined in, while the oven indicator went into reverse as the temperature dropped. It was downdraught, an all too familiar outcome of rain and low pressure, the guarantee of a disastrous dinner. Fortunately, I had the back-up of a Calor gas cooker kept in the scullery awaiting just such an emergency, so I heated it up and transferred the dinner to it, leaving the Lady Mayoress' nut roast in the Rayburn where it would still cook in the lower heat. Half an hour later when I checked on the lamb and roast potatoes, there they were, lukewarm and uncooked. The gas had run out. I am always dumbfounded when this happens because it is so unpredictable, there being no warning. Men walk on the moon, monkeys orbit the earth in spacecraft, but no simple warning has ever been invented to warn when the Calor gas runs out.

I slipped into my boots and, pinny flying in the wind, clumped across the yard to collect a new cylinder from an outside shed, fixing it on to the stove in double-quick time. The five ginger working cats with their saturated coats could not be blamed for nipping inside with the back door left open, but I blamed them good and proper when a fight broke out under the kitchen table and flying bits of ginger fur joined the smuts from the fire.

By now the cooking conditions were less than ideal, with the standards plummeting well below those prescribed by the Department of Health. I slapped the pastry lid on the gooseberry tart and fervently hoped there was nothing nasty trapped underneath it. The Lady Mayoress would be bound to get it. I should have warned the guests that dinner would be late because, spot on time, I could hear the chairs in the dining room scraping back as they all took their places. I hoped the F/H/B would turn up and engage them all in conversation whilst I concentrated on more practical matters. Eventually the hungry diners, obviously seeking information, despatched one of the two small sons of the deserted wife, to the kitchen on reconnaissance. I savagely ignored him as he fell into step behind me, dogging every hurried move, and picking up my mutterings. I was relieved, though it was short-lived, when he suddenly took off on an imaginary motor-bike, vroom-vrooming through the kitchen door into the dining room, then vroom-vrooming round the long table, chanting over and over, at the top of his voice, the words he had heard me mumbling to myself. 'Her wouldn't have none of us if 'tweren't for the money!' Vroom, vroom, 'Her wouldn't have...' etc, etc. Vroom, vroom!

I had to face them when dinner was eventually dished up, but only Fred and Doris thought it funny and could not stop laughing. The Valium lady picked at her lamb and spoonful of courgettes with cheese sauce, and reached for her pills, the two boys loudly voiced their preference for a Big Mac and the Lady Mayoress tackled her nut roast vigorously.

I found it hard to concentrate, my mind was back in the stable with Tom's horse. Why did he have to die, why had he stretched to get at that light switch so far out of his reach?

'Would you like the cheeseboard, Mr Gordon?'

He was only four years old, all his life in front of him.

'Milk or cream, Mrs Fogerty?'

Poor Tom, after all that care and work, and just the insurance money at the end of it.

I was glad to get to bed that night, I felt so drained and exhausted. As usual, I slept heavily. At least nothing ever interfered with that.

Friday turned out to be a slightly better day, dull and overcast, but dry, which cheered them all up. On Saturday they all left for home, the Lady Mayoress remarking it had been the most er, er, unusual holiday she had ever taken, and next week at the banquet she might even mention it to Princess Alexandra. 'Perhaps Princess Alexandra will come for a holiday,' I said to the F/H/B as they all disappeared homewards. 'I bleddy well hope not,' he answered. 'Not on Ma Fogerty's recommend,' adding thoughtfully, 'not that you'll ever see they again.' He was right. We didn't.

Chapter Six

It was Saturday morning and I was standing on the bed in the single room holding a tin bucket in one hand and a paintbrush in the other, slapping whitewash on a big dark patch spreading across the ceiling. Friday nights in August often turned out to be stormy, with high winds followed by torrential rain, and although a heavy sleeper, my ears had become attuned to the crash of a falling slate. That particular night it must have registered with the F/H/B because he stirred in his sleep beside me and muttered, 'I'll murder they puppies in the morning, see if I don't.' The puppies' list of misdeeds was extensive but it seemed a touch unjust of the F/H/B to blame them for being on the roof in the small hours, ripping off slates just for the hell of it. I wanted to tell him this but decided against it, as wives instinctively know when to speak and when not to speak, although I recalled more than once being nudged from a deep sleep to hear a voice intoning, 'Hark to that rain, Maid!'

I knew I must remember when I took the morning tea round on Saturday to scan the ceilings for the tell-tale wet patch that signified the missing slate, then mark it down for a quick cover-up job before any new guests arrived.

I often used to long for a mellow September when each weekend in August seemed stormier than the previous one, and the F/H/B swore he heard me welcome the new intake regularly with the words, 'You should have been here last week! Last week it rained, but not this bad.'

I endeavoured never to mention the actual word 'rain', as it would have a depressing effect on holidaymakers, and this made me more devious than a politician, never giving a straight answer. The first question they always asked when I took their early morning tea to their rooms on a foggy, drizzly/blowy day was always about the weather. After carefully putting down the tray I would stride over to the window, draw back the curtains, and say something casual, like, 'Oh, 'tis one of they old Exmoor days,' and then bolt for the door. Old friends, who knew all about 'they old Exmoor days' would drink their tea and pull the bedclothes over their heads until breakfast time, whilst new guests would still be resting on one elbow and staring at the window, wondering what an Exmoor day was.

A bookie friend of ours, who spent many holidays at Chilcott, says he always remembers that Elvis Presley died on a wet day in August, because, in reply to the usual question, I answered just that. 'Elvis Presley's died!'

Another political deviation was to shift the onus on to somebody else. Like 'the postman reckons 'tis likely to improve,' which was probably a half-truth, with the postman adding 'in a coupla weeks'. The F/H/B brushed aside such pleasantries with a more practical, 'What h'odds about the weather, so long's you'm breathing.'

It usually took more than bad weather to restrain the hardier type of holidaymaker, who don backpacks and sturdy boots to explore the moors. They appreciate Exmoor, although many agree there is a dark side to it when there are lowering clouds and skies with more than a hint of menace. The beauty of the scenery can be cast in shadows, the thunder roll unendingly and flashes of low lightning silence the sky-larks in their heather nests.

Thus it was on 15 August 1952, when the moors were submerged under torrents of water and the little resort of Lynmouth was flooded, drowning 28 people and many livestock, destroying homes and hotels. That terrible date is never far from the memories of those who survived that frightening night. In Dulverton there is a plaque marking the height where the River Barle overflowed, 20 feet above normal, washing away two cottages.

So there I was on that Saturday morning in August, standing in my socks on a newspaper on the bed, slapping whitewash on the ceiling, when my thoughts were interrupted by a sound which could have been 'Coo-ee'. I listened, and from downstairs came another 'Coo-ee', followed by ''tis only us, popped in to see you.' I climbed off the bed, spread the newspaper carefully on the floor, placed the tin bucket and paintbrush on it, and went to investigate. As I reached the back stairs I looked down on to a small crowd of grinning, upturned faces. They were unfamiliar.

Then a beaming, lady spokeswoman enquired, 'Remember us? We came here once with Bill and Mary from Barnstaple, and you said to pop in any time we're passing. These are our friends that we ramble with and we're all *gasping* for a cup of your nice coffee. Can I help get out the cups – there's eight of us, so that'll be nine – yes, of course you're going to have one with us, make the most of a bit of company when you got it, I always say. Now, where's your kettle? What, no electric kettle, however do you manage just with that old stove... and did you know you've white spots all over, oh, and I nearly forgot, one of them pups outside's had diarrhoea all over your front doorstep. I should clear it up now, dear, you know, before somebody come... is that a car – your first arrivals? Fancy coming this early, and with *that* on your doorstep, some folks just don't think... We've never forgot that fruit cake you brought out last time we came, have we, Bert?'

If Friday nights were the worst in August, then Saturday was usually the worst day, any likely disasters seemingly saving themselves for the weekend.

One such occasion was when our much-loved baker selected Chilcott, as luck would have it, to stage a notable collapse. A pleasant, reliable, middle-aged Christian bachelor, he drove his van from Barnstaple to deliver bread and cakes every Tuesday and Saturday, ploughing through snow in winter, thunderstorms in summer, punctures and breakdowns, cheerfully hindered by little old ladies with rheumaticky fingers who wanted rabbits skinned, posting letters, and bringing all the gossip from the Great Outside.

The first indication that all was not quite as it should be on that particular hot, sultry Saturday morning, came when I made our baker his usual pot of tea. He was sitting on the old settle and I was about to hand him his cup and a slice of jam sponge (mine, not his, he never touched his own confections) when he very slowly switched from the vertical to the horizontal, lying the full length of the settle. I ran over and grabbed his shoulders, hauling him back to a sitting position. 'Mr Crump!' I shouted in panic. 'Are you all right?' Mr Crump was plainly not all right. His face was flushed scarlet and his eyes stared straight ahead as he muttered 'I'm bad, Missus, my God I'm bad.'

The heat in the kitchen was intense, with the sun blistering through the window and the Rayburn stoked up high for cooking. Out, I thought wildly, I must get him out, somewhere cooler... the sitting room, shady and restful, an armchair by the window in a cool breeze, that was it. 'Mr Crump!' I yelled, so that it registered. 'I'm taking you to the sitting room, 'tis a bit cooler there.' Mr Crump's eyes swivelled neither to the right nor to the left, but just stared fixedly ahead, like a zombie. It had to be a seizure of some sort, something I had never encountered in a human being before, although I could recall sheep now and again that turned starey-eyed at shearing time. Sometimes they died. Poor Mr Crump, with a seizure. And on a Saturday, his busy day as well as mine. A Tuesday would have been better.

Mr Crump's homely face looked like it might burst into flames. Somehow I had to get him out of that kitchen. With what amounted to superhuman strength I tugged him off the settle by his Mothers Pride overall and on to his feet, then, locked together like a couple of shuffling drunks, we weaved our way through the kitchen, across the dining room, down two steps into the cider room, over the flagstones and reached, at last, the coolness of the sitting room. 27 paces that seemed like a marathon.

I eased the baker into the armchair by the window and raced back to the sink for a glass of water. I returned more steadily, aware that I was trailing a watery route, by now owing as much to stress as speed, only to find Mr Crump totally collapsed, with his arms dangling lifeless over the arms of the chair. He's gone, I thought wildly, but no, not with that colour, he couldn't be, he looked so hot still. I moistened his lips with the water and sprinted to the sink again, holding the dishcloth under the cold tap, then back to spread it, dripping, across his forehead. I wondered if Mr Crump's past life was flashing before his eyes. Mine certainly was. I remembered with amazing clarity when I was a teenager in the Girls Life Brigade, and how I had spurned First Aid in favour of playing a flute in the band. Well, poor Mr Crump was now paying the price for my selfishness. Get a doctor, I thought. And then remembered there was not a bed in the place that was made. Supposing he died, right there in the window. His lips were moving. I bent low to catch his words. 'I'm going,' he gasped, 'I'm going.'

'No you're not,' I told him, trying to sound positive.

'You're going to get better, you'll see.'

'I'm going,' he persisted. 'I'm going to... to telephone.'

'No, Mr Crump, no,' I insisted. 'I'll do it for you. I'll get a doctor, then I'll call your brother and let him know that you're all right.'

I knew he lived with his brother and sister-in-law somewhere in Barnstaple. The baker lifted a limp hand, almost agitatedly, and waved it from side to side. His lips moved again. 'I don't want no doctor and I don't want me brother, I just wants to ring Porlock.' He made a feeble attempt to stand, but fell back in the chair again. 'You'd bestways do it for me, Missus, if you'd be so good. 'Tis Porlock 900, you got that?'

Porlock? Surely he meant Barnstaple.

He laboured on. 'And if a woman answers, tell her...' His voice trailed off.

'Yes, yes, Mr Crump, you just tell me.'

'Tell her I loves her.'

My hand fell from the brow I'd been mopping with the dishcloth. I had assumed that any message would be to his relations, especially if he was worried it might be his last. Financial, possibly, like a little hidey-hole in the mattress stuffed with his Christmas tips, or a few words of gratitude at the end. Mr Crump in love was a bombshell. He was our baker, Mothers Pride, and I never thought of him having a lifestyle outside his bread round, other than Chapel on a Sunday and skittles on a Wednesday. 'Porlock 900,' he whispered, adding in a stronger, more matter-of-fact voice. 'And don't you go getting me no doctor. ''Tis me heart that's aching all right, but not the way you'll be thinking!' He closed his eyes again and sank back into the cushions, as though the whole effort had been too much for him .

Running to the telephone in the kitchen, I dialled the number. A woman did answer. 'Yes, hello, Porlock 900.' I gurgled, suddenly speechless, and said nothing. 'Mr Crump loves you,' did not come trippingly off the tongue, alternatively, 'the baker loves you' had too formal a ring for such a tender message. 'Mr Crump,' I commenced. 'Yes?' queried the friendly voice. I had a flash of inspiration. 'Mr Crump would like a word with you, just hold on for a minute.' Back in the sitting room the baker was still slumped in the armchair, head back, eyes closed. I shook his arm. 'She wants a word with you,' I said firmly, and to my relief he struggled from the chair and managed to lurch dizzily to the kitchen, without resorting to our drunken two-step. Almost before he had snatched the telephone he was trumpeting 'Pet, Pet, I loves yer, I loves yer,' and, as if to add emphasis, he burst into noisy sobs.

I crept away upstairs, sensing that the real drama, far from being over, was only just commencing.

At last I was able to get on with the bed-making, although after the interesting turn of events I had both ears cocked for any snatches of the lovers' tiff that drifted out through the downstairs window and up to the bedrooms. 'I never meaned it, Pet, you got to believe me,' followed by more wracking sobs. Then came, 'I got to see yer... how can I... is yer husband out tonight?' I started to smile. It was changing from high drama to farce. Our dear Chapel-going, hymn-singing Mr Crump was in love. And with a married woman! Pulling the top sheet over the pillows on the four-poster, I collapsed across the bed howling with laughter. Five minutes later I was still lying there, still laughing, when the F/H/B poked his head round the door. 'What the hell's going on, that's what I want to know,' he demanded. 'I just come in for me dinner and what do I find?' His voice rose an octave at the injustice of it. 'There's old Crump crying on the telephone, you up yer in bed in the middle of the day, and me with no bleddy dinner.'

I slid off the bed, wiping my eyes on a corner of the sheet, as I tried to explain the sequence of the mornings events, finishing with, 'And how can us sit down there at the table eating our dinner, with all that going on right beside us?'

'How long's it bin now?' he wanted to know.

'Best part of the hour, I shouldn't wonder.'

'Well, then,' said the F/H/B practically, 'he can't keep that rattle up fer much longer. Come on, Maid, I wants me dinner, and if I don't get it in the next ten minutes there'll be another bleddy uproar.'

Apprehensively, I entered the kitchen to find the situation seemed to have cooled a little, though Mr Crump was still trumpeting, 'I'll always love yer, Pet, you knows that, I got to see yer tonight, if I can manage it.'

'And if you can't manage it, tell her I will,' interrupted the F/H/B.

The baker turned at this intrusion, and, realising he had company, lingeringly wound up the conversation. 'Say it, Pet, say it now, just say it... course I does, always will...'

There followed three little squeaky sounds, then the receiver was carefully replaced and he turned to face us. I felt mesmerised, no longer seeing the quiet, respectable Chapel-going man I had known for years, but a mad, passionate lover in the throes of an affair with a married woman.

I was throwing a salad together whilst the F/H/B carved three plates of beef from a cold joint, one of which he slid along the table towards Mr Crump. Get that down you,' he ordered. 'And for God's sake pull yourself together. You'm like an old sheep with a worm on 'ees brain.'

The baker, recovered and smiling now, seized a knife and fork and manfully tackled his dinner, reliving, between mouthfuls, and with a certain zest, the tale of his collapse.

'Your Missus thought I was pretty near daid, didn't 'ee, Missus?' he said, prodding his laden fork in my direction.

I confessed that he had me worried.

'No woman's worth all that upset,' declared the F/H/B.

'Not to have the screamin' hab-dabs over.'

''Twas a seizure,' I corrected. He was overcome with a seizure.'

'You call it what you like, and I'll call it what I like,' pursued the F/H/B.

The argument was halted by a knock at the back door, followed by the appearance of the first guests of the day. They were four old friends, and we were delighted to welcome them, but why, we wondered, had they used the back door instead of the front? 'We couldn't drive any further,' they explained. 'A bakery van was blocking the road and the doors were open, and there was this great big pig looking in the back, so we shoo-ed it down the road into the yard and shut the gate on it. Did we do the right thing?'

'God Almighty,' yelped the baker, leaping to his feet. 'It coulda cleared the lot.' And with surprising agility in one who had seemed to hover between life and death only a short while before, he shot out through the back door. I was torn between waiting to hear the extent of the pig's temptation and rushing upstairs to finish the rooms. I compromised by making a large pot of tea and settling the visitors round the table. I feared it was not Mr Crump's lucky day from the volume of his anguished wail outside, which was loud enough to float over the hill and down through the next valley.

'Me marshmallers,' he cried. 'There's teeth marks in me marshmallers!'

He came through the doorway carrying a large wooden tray of chocolate marshmallows, still in passably neat rows, every one indented with teeth marks.

'It don't say a lot for your bleddy ol' cakes if the pig tried 'em all and never ate one of 'em,' observed the F/H/B.

'What shall I do with 'em?' demanded Mr Crump. 'Nobody'll buy they with teeth marks all over.'

'Aw, chuck 'em in our pig bucket and write it off as education,' directed the F/H/B. ''Tis the price o' love you'm paying for. Nort don't come cheap these days.'

I poured the baker a cup of tea as he mournfully emptied his marshmallows into the pig bucket. He looked upset. 'Don't worry,' I told him. 'I'll mix 'em up with some tater skins, they'll eat 'em all right then.'

The visitors moved out to sit in the garden until their rooms were ready, and as I was going upstairs I could hear the F/H/B offering the baker a bit of homespun advice on the perils of letting women interfere in a chap's working life.

Chapter Seven

We always keep a couple of horses on the farm, a fairish hunter for the F/H/B and a smaller, all-round pony big enough for me to ride, but quiet enough for children and to loan to guests. Therefore, it was a major tragedy when my pony, Gay Cavalier, died of old age at twenty-two, though, truth to tell, he scarcely fitted all his requirements. He was a handsome fellow, looking like a well-bred racehorse in miniature, and he was sweet-tempered, patiently doddling up and down the lane all day, giving children rides, but as soon as a more experienced rider took to the saddle he would launch into his routine of frantic head-tossing, accompanied by a frightening squeaking, then dance sideways, bucking, rearing, and, almost inevitably, bolting. He had splendid action, being what the F/H/B called a 'daisy-picker', with his hooves skimming over the turf and scarcely appearing to leave the ground. I had bought him as a five-year-old and loved him so much I could never bear to part with him, although he threw me off so many times I finally lost my nerve and refused to ride him again. He threw every adult off, even the F/H/B, who was a first-class horseman, came home from exercise one day looking like he had been tarred and feathered from head to toe, except that 'twas mud and dead leaves he was covered in.

It was a mystery to me why Gay Cavalier turned out to be so wild, as the day I bought him I rode for miles to try him out and he never put a foot wrong, in fact he was a perfect ride.

'Why?' I asked the F/H/B, who had done a bit of horse-dealing himself occasionally. 'Because, Maid,' he explained heavily, 'he must've been shut in the stable and starved for a couple of days and that'll calm down any hoss. He'll walk out that door quiet's a mouse and you never finds out no different 'til a week arter you bought and paid for'n. 'Tis easier to find a second-hand woman than a second-hand hoss, danged if 'tain't.' He shook his head disbelievingly at being caught with an old con trick. With hindsight, perhaps I should have been more cautious myself. I clearly remembered the pony's registered name on his papers as Lucifer, which at the time I considered unsuitable and changed to Gay Cavalier. Country folks say you should never change a name, and if ever the devil was in anything, it was that pony.

Nevertheless, he had a kind eye and was good natured, being so friendly and orderly in his stable that he lulled would-be riders into thinking that they could handle him. Visitors were informed of his past history and all rode at their own risk, with many paying the penalty for over-confidence. He was the cause of a lot of hurt pride, but, miraculously, no bones were ever broken, the nastiest accident being to a smashing lady called Rita who suffered a back injury that put her in hospital for a month. She still came back to Chilcott for holidays but gave up riding and took up golf.

Some, in particular teenagers, were eager to prove they had some riding experience but there was a large gap between the passable riders and the ones who thought they could ride. Most of the passable riders knew something of horses and listened intently to the F/H/B instructions, whilst the others tended to take off like bats out of hell, screaming 'Watch me, Mummy!'

Louisa was clearly one of the latter, black curls tossing, beautifully turned out from the top of her velvet cap to the tip of her shining leather jodhpur boots, her every whim attended to by an adoring Mummy (Daddy was never mentioned). She was directed to ride only in the lane where there is a high hedge each side, to safeguard her from Gay Cavalier veering off course. Louisa's reply was that Mummy had spent hundreds of pounds having her taught to ride by Alan Oliver's sister, from the famous showjumping family, and she trotted off defiantly, straight into our neighbour's field at the bottom of the lane, where the pony at once set up with his squeaking and prancing routine, and finally bolted straight across the field. Out of control, he crashed into a five-bar gate, mercifully not injuring himself, and deposited his rider on the ground.

The F/H/B arrived on the scene and looked down on the winded Louisa. 'How much is Alan Oliver's sister's lessons worth now, then?' he inquired.

Louisa sat up. 'He bucked me off,' she said indignantly.

'He did not buck you off,' was the F/H/B's answer. 'You falled off because you ain't a good enough rider to stop on, so don't give me that ol' guff. And look at the damage you done to that gate. And if ort happened to that pony 'twould hev bin your fault. You just count yerself bleddy lucky you got away wi' it.'

Louisa did not show up for dinner that night and neither did she apologise but Mummy explained she was too upset after the way Mr Huxtable had spoken to her. 'That's up to her,' said Mr Huxtable uncaringly.

The dessert that evening was lemon meringue pie, topped with clotted cream. 'Louisa's favourite,' cried Mummy. 'I'll take some up to her room.'

'Oh no you don't,' disagreed the F/H/B. 'When Louisa comes down and sits at this table, and eats her dinner in a proper manner, then she can have the dessert, and not before, and you can tell her I said so.' Mummy lapsed into a stunned silence, but luckily the next day they were leaving anyway. We never heard from them again.

⊷◆⊶

Townsfolk moving to live in the country often seem to think it obligatory to place a Land Rover and horse-trailer at the top of their shopping list. Next comes the horse, irrespective of whether they can ride or not.

Such a one was a former guest at our farm who had been willed what sounded like a hefty sum, and on the strength of it decided to move from London to Exmoor. He purchased a swish little property with a paddock and stables and then true to pattern this was followed by the Land Rover and a new two-horse trailer. He then announced he would be looking to spend a thousand pounds on a 'smart little hunter' and as sound travels faster than light in these parts, every horse dealer for miles found he unexpectedly had a 'smart little hunter' for sale that had been up-valued overnight to £1000.

The F/H/B, returning home from Taunton market one Saturday afternoon, met the would-be horseman some way from his new home, slumped ungracefully across the back of an old grey Irish mare.

'I'm just trying her out,' explained the rider. 'She's rather jolly, don't you think?'

'No, I bleddy don't,' replied the F/H/B. 'How much be 'em asking fer that thing?'

'Oh, it's £1000, but I might well get a good deal, 50 quid knocked off, with luck. I like to think I drive a hard bargain, doncher know.'

'That thing's fit for one place, and one place only,' the F/H/B told him. 'And that's up Bristol in the knackers yard. And the first thing you want to do, afore you buys any horse, is to learn to ride.'

The upshot of it all was that the following week our new countryman, taking heed of the F/H/B's advice turned up for a riding lesson on our pony. The F/H/B planned to teach him to sit properly in the saddle, and would give him his lesson round our smallest paddock where he could come to no harm.

However, at the last minute the F/H/B had been called away to a funeral so it was left to me to catch and saddle Gay Cavalier. There was more delay than I bargained for as I felt obliged to spruce the pony up a bit, so impressed was I with his rider's smart appearance. He looked like a male model for a glossy advertisement in *Horse and Hound*, immaculately turned out in pristine white breeches, shining black leather boots that must have cost hundreds, a well-cut tweed hacking jacket, a brand new velvet cap, and, the finishing touch, a spotted silk cravat round his neck.

He mounted easily enough, being long-legged, and together we circled the paddock a few times. He was doing well, so I let him go and he sat straight in the saddle, walking and trotting on his own, which was simple enough in such a confined area. It was a morale- boosting exercise and my pupil, fired with enthusiasm, thought he would like to ride to the top of the lane. Cavalier was undoubtedly on his best behaviour, his rider was greatly improved and there was the additional safety of the high hedges to keep him on course. I opened the yard gate for the pony to go out and his rider called back over his shoulder, 'My word, Norma, what a difference, already I feel so confident.'

These might almost have been his last words, because fifteen minutes later, chastened and bedraggled, he returned, walking stiffly down the road, leading his mount by the reins.

By that time friends from Barnstaple had turned up and I was in the kitchen buttering yeast cake so I shouted to leave the pony in the stable and come in for tea.

Our rider presented a doleful sight as he entered the kitchen; the white breeches were mud-spattered, the jaunty little spotted cravat had twice as many spots and he was carrying his battered velvet cap from which, dead centre, a whole square of material, like a little two-inch window, was missing. As his story unfolded, it was obvious that his new-found confidence had been his undoing. Near the top of the lane, he told us, he had decided to light up a cigarette, so, dropping the reins on the pony's neck, he stuck the cigarette in his mouth and struck a match. He might as well have lit the blue touch paper to a rocket, Gay Cavalier swung into one of his instant party pieces, practice having perfected a gigantic leap in the air with arched back and all four feet off the ground at once, then bolting.

With no reins to hang on to, horse and rider parted company almost at once, and a passing farmer in a Land Rover blocked the road and managed to catch the runaway whilst his jockey was still picking himself off the tarmac. The epic account took some time to relate to the appreciative audience and I fervently wished my pupil would get on with his tea and be gone before the F/H/B returned. I felt we were both likely to face a severe interrogation from that quarter. After a second cup of tea and another slice of yeast cake, he finally got up to go and turned for the door, displaying to us all a tear the size of a pig's ear in the backside of his muddy breeches. Revealed underneath were red, white and blue Union Jack under-pants. None of us had the heart to tell him the fate of his new breeches and everybody managed a polite goodbye, holding back raucous laughter until he was well out of earshot.

To our New Man's credit, he bounced back with breeches neatly repaired, boots shining and the hunting cap replaced with an expensive bowler. He persevered with his lessons then squandered his inheritance on a whole string of indifferent horses, which finished his marriage and lost him his smallholding. Warnings from the F/H/B that horse trading is a mug's game went unheeded, with it all ending in a sad but familiar pattern.

Gay Cavalier died one warm, moonlight night, collapsing on to his favourite patch of grass in Cow Field. He was twenty-two years old and must have suffered a heart attack. We both walked down in the moonlight to bid goodbye to our old friend. I kissed him but didn't linger while the F/H/B caressed his ears and stayed with him.

◇◇◆◇◇

The farm seemed strangely deserted without Gay Cavalier's larger-than-life presence and the following spring we knew we must search for a replacement, both for the visitors' use and as company for the other horse, Suzy, who disliked being on her own.

As most business on Exmoor is conducted by word of mouth we put it about that we were looking for a pony, half expecting results within hours. Nothing happened. Time was going on so we took to answering one or two newspaper advertisements although we were warned by other horse-owners that, for sheer exaggeration, horse advertising was in a class of its own. They were right.

The first we went to see was described as a 'brown gelding with great potential,' whose great potential lay in the direction of hurling his rider further than any other brown gelding in the world.

'A gorgeous schoolmaster with plenty of bone' sounded a must but £2000 was well over the top for two or three trips a week round the turnip field.

A 'mature gelding' was next on our visiting list, looking all of two weeks off the knackers yard, whilst an 'educated little mare' appeared to be able to dance, effecting an odd rhythm, three steps forward then back one. Watching the F/H/B canter past I could almost hum a tune to one, two, three and then back, one, two, three and then back. The owner could see the little horse was badly mis-behaving but as the F/H/B pulled up to dismount still gamely attempted to push a sale, volunteering, 'This little mare was placed third at Exford Show.' 'Well, if I'd bin judge,' said the F/H/B, sliding wearily from the saddle, 'I'd hev put her bottom.'

'You shouldn't have hurt his feelings,' I admonished him as we walked back to the pig van. He was unrepentant. 'If they can't face the truth it serves 'em right,' he avowed.

We seemed to be travelling ever-increasing distances in our never-ending search for a genuine pony and one evening found us some 50 miles off Exmoor, booked in to view a 'promising grey, ideal for a lady, with a snaffle mouth and lovely floating action.' The stable yard was so smart and spotless, with tubs of daffodils dotted here and there, that the pig van looked sadly out of place.

The promising grey was led out for our inspection by what the F/H/B all too obviously considered a promising young woman, a striking, well-built, Scandinavian-style blonde. 'Bootiful,' he breathed as she led the grey forwards and backwards, quickening to a trot that did amazing things to her figure. 'She's been ver' well handled,' the vision purred huskily. 'I can see that,' answered the F/H/B with a smile that was next-door to a leer, as his eyes never wrenched from the sleek hips in the tight breeches. 'Where's the saddle, me dear, us'll git my missus up fer a try-out.'

Such was the buzz between my man and the transfixing blonde, that I jibbed a bit at trotting off into the sunset, leaving the two of them together to watch the grass grow. It seemed to me a safer idea to get the seductive lady doing the trotting-off leaving me to have a quiet word with the F/H/B.

She was charmingly acquiescent to my request, putting the mare through her paces in an adjoining field and I had to admit grudgingly, and only to myself, that I had never watched a smarter combination. The grey was a little beauty, narrow and well-bred, with an intelligent head and flowing mane and tail, and lived up to the advertised description of 'lovely, floating action'.

I turned to berate my man for the leers he had been dishing in the direction of the luscious lady, and got no further than 'You doughbake...' when we were joined by a portly, middle-aged man who introduced himself as the owner of the stables. From the fond smile he directed at his groom as she trotted past, he owned both horse and rider as well. The big man was there to talk business and it was patently a formula that should have worked well, the stunning girl fronting the sale initially, followed by the Big Boss, all guns firing, to clinch a deal that would have kept us in groceries for the next ten years. The F/H/B was forthright in saying that sort of sum was way over our heads, but the attention then shifted to me, women often being an easier touch than their menfolk, particularly if the horse is genuine and has looks that appeal.

The Big Man switched to me, smiling, saying, 'Now then, missus, I reckon on you wanting to try out that little mare. No obligation, mind, no obligation at all, but just you try her then tell us what you think.'

He beckoned to the rider to pull up and with a great show of helping her to dismount, managed to slide his hands the length of her body. Her lips brushed his ear in passing and she giggled and whispered. I felt I shouldn't be staring, awkward and gauche, at such an intimate little scene, but then it was all over and Miss Scandinavia was devoting all her attention to the F/H/B. The Big Man heaved me into the saddle by my welly boot, shortened the stirrups, and I set off across the field, loving every minute. The grey was narrow which meant my sturdy legs for once hung downwards instead of sticking out sideways, and with the evening breeze in my face the whole exercise was bliss. I ignored the F/H/B and the big blonde; in fact I hoped the longer they chatted, the longer I could ride but when I looked across and saw him waving his hat at me I knew I had better pull up.

I dismounted without any help and the owner said, 'You looked very good on my little mare, very good, indeed, didn't she Annette?' 'Ver' good,' declared the glamour queen. 'Zey are made for each ozzer.' They both knew I hadn't looked half as good as she had, and the F/H/B said as much. 'Sorry, Squire,' he told the Big Man. 'The money's too much, the hoss is too good fer what us want 'n fer and to cap it all my missus and that hoss don't match up.'

I stared in disbelief at the injustice of the F/H/B's statement, and was stung into the query. 'How do you mean, us don't match up?' ''Cos your backside's bigger than the hoss's,' he asserted matter-of-factly.

Annette and the Big Man smiled politely, accepting what must have been the most conclusive termination of any horse deal in history. I imagined the minute we rattled off in the pig van they would roll about the yard laughing.

Our journey home was somewhat less than cordial.

'You carried on like a goggle-eyed doughbake with that maid,' was my opening shot.

'You've got a helluva imagination, you have,' was the surly rejoinder.

'That's right, deny everything, after I seen it with me own eyes. And fancy saying that about my backside being fatter than the horse's.'

'So 'ee was, and who's fault's that?'

'Well, all right, but you didn't have to say so, not in front of they.'

The F/H/B concentrated on his steering.

'No wonder fellas hev they old pair maids,' he thought aloud.

''Tis oh pair, not old pair,' I contradicted.

'That's what I said, old pair, and don't pick me up when I've said it right. Cor, they'm saxy all right.'

'They was carrying on, him and her, you could tell.'

'The rotten, filthy, dirty lucky bugger,' observed my husband.

'She didn't sound so saxy when he helped her off that horse. I heard every word.'

'Well, go on, then, you'm dying to tell me.'

'No, I'm not.'

'Bleddy well don't, then.'

'She said, 'Take your big hand off my bum.''

'Her spoke very good English,' said the F/H/B.

The rest of the journey seemed a long way to travel in silence.

◇◆◇

The following Tuesday, Seemingly looked in to tell us he had heard of a good pony for sale, at a reasonable price, up on the coastal side of the moor at a place called Glenthorne.

''Tis bootiful,' he told us.

'You talking about the hoss or the place?' the F/H/B wanted to know.

'The place, you old vool,' said Seemingly irritably. 'I ain't seen the hoss, have I?'

'I dunno. How'm I s'posed to know where you bin or what you seen?' queried the F/H/B. ''Ee could be a bleddy donkey in a circus fer all us know.'

''Ee's genuine,' retorted Seemingly. 'And that's as much as I can tell 'ee. I heard about'n up Cutcombe yesterday. Yer, I tell 'ee what, I'll come with 'ee to see'n, I can't say fairer than that.'

We made an appointment for the following evening and as we then had two guests staying asked them if they would mind an early dinner. Then, if they liked, they could come along with us afterwards to see the pony, to which they readily agreed. Mr and Mrs Wild, like so many others over the years, had turned from visitors into friends and had fitted in with our excursions many times before. They were a pleasant, middle-aged couple, who owned a newsagency in Lancashire, working long hours seven days a week, but taking a break on Exmoor as often as possible.

They liked the idea of an evening trip across the moor with a bit of horse dealing tacked on the end. 'Ee, we done some things on holiday,' enthused Mr Wild, 'but never owt like that.' Then a little anxiously, 'We won't be late back, I take it? You know us, like, for our bed.'

Indeed, I did, they were always among the first guests to bid their goodnights but were always up early in the morning walking Rusty, their curly-coated setter, across the fields. Then it was back to a hearty breakfast, make their own bed, and leave their room immaculate. Perfect visitors. I assured them we would be back in good time, because, although we ourselves were none too familiar with the coastline bordering the Bristol Channel, Seemingly would be with us to point the way.

We heaved a couple of bales of straw into the pig van to seat the passengers then Mr and Mrs Wild and I climbed in the back, leaving the front seat for our guide. The F/H/B's first stop was to pick up Seemingly, who was already waiting at his gate dressed in his best go-to-market tweeds and pork-pie hat.

It was a lovely evening, and fascinating, as the seasons always are, to see that winter was fast changing to spring, the bracken greening up, with great splashes of golden gorse here and there, as though a mad painter had wildly daubed colour on a glorious canvas. One or two of the moorland ponies had foals at foot and a couple of startled deer almost ran into us. Mr and Mrs Wild were openly envious that we lived in such a place and we told them we considered ourselves privileged and tried never to take it for granted. The F/H/B steered the pig van from one dazzling panorama to the next, until the north Devon coastline unfolded, with the mountains of Wales misty in the distance across the Bristol Channel.

Seemingly directed us to the turning for Glenthorne and we bumped down a narrow, tree-lined track that looked as though we were heading straight out to sea. We arrived after a ten-minute drive at a large mellow-stoned house bathed in the evening sunlight, perched on the edge of cliffs that dropped down sheer about 250 feet to the lashing sea below. The lawns and gardens were spectacular. A terrace running along the front of the house with pillars and stone statues every few yards gave it an almost unreal appearance, almost like an Italian film set. There was a massive oak entrance door with a rustic bridge over a stream leading to it. Somehow, it all managed to look artless and uncontrived, as though it had just happened that way.

A couple were walking towards us carrying a saddle and bridle and we all introduced ourselves. They were Ben and Caroline Halliday, the owners of Glenthorne, and they explained they felt guilty at offering the pony for sale as he belonged to their daughter, who was away at college but there seemed no point in keeping him any longer. He was an old family retainer, well thought of and without vice.

They were a charming couple, insisting that we all enjoy the view whilst they themselves caught the pony in the little field at the back. We stood in a row, gazing out to sea as though mesmerised at little sailing boats bobbing near the shore, whilst further out a great ship steamed up the Channel, and overhead raucous screeches from gulls mingled with the chatter of small birds in a row of poplars.

There was a clip-clop behind us as Mr Halliday led the pony up for our inspection. One glance was enough to see this was the big disappointment of the evening. He was outstandingly plain, with an over-large head on a thick neck, a short, heavy frame, and hairy legs leading down to hooves the size of dinner plates. 'This is our dear old Wellington,' said Mrs Halliday fondly.

I searched for something to say that would not sound hurtful. 'I'm sorry,' I said. 'I'll not waste your time trying him because I can see he's not what I'm looking for. He would be a replacement for a pony that's died you see and this one's nothing like...' I felt I was floundering.

Mrs Halliday's finely-boned face looked crestfallen.

'He's not really up to a lot of riding,' she said apologetically. 'He's quite old, and he needs a home and cherishing and as my daughter's not here... I know he's not worth much, and he's been a good servant for a lot of years, and...' she glanced at her husband, 'well, we're not getting any younger.' Her voice trailed. The F/H/B ran his hand down Wellington's legs, searching for something charitable to say about the old horse.

'He's sound enough,' was the best he could do.

'He'd seemingly make a good enough trekking pony, jes working summers,' volunteered Seemingly.

The Hallidays looked at one another across the pony's back and the wife shook her head as though an unspoken joint decision had been reached. 'He's not for trekking,' she declared, patting the greying muzzle. 'In fact, he's not for anything. It was cruel and stupid of us to even consider parting with our old servant. So...' She smiled at her husband, 'Take these good people indoors, dear, whilst I put the old boy away, and then we'll celebrate.'

We protested that as no deal had been clinched there could be nothing to celebrate. Mr Halliday thought otherwise. 'It's such a relief,' he told us. 'We knew we should get rid of the old chap but at the same time – well, you know how it is, and looking at him through your eyes this evening, somehow he didn't look as appealing as one thought...and as for trekking, well, it just made us think again, that's all.' His voice took on a happy chord. 'So now you're all here, we'll celebrate Wellington's long and happy retirement!'

We followed our host through the great oak door into a small, medieval banqueting hall with traditional domed roof. A solid oak staircase curved up out of sight with suits of armour lodged like sentinels on every third or fourth stair. Mr Halliday led us to the right through a green leather door into the library, a unique circular room, with shelves packed with books from floor to ceiling, and before the window, a round table with an array of glasses and bottles.

Mr and Mrs Wild looked mesmerised at the wonder of it all, as indeed we were. Our hostess joined us, happy and laughing, and her husband proffered drinks. Mr Wild looked at his wife. 'I think I would like a sweet sherry, please,' she said. 'But only a very small one.' 'Er, yes, that'll be champion,' agreed Mr Wild. Seemingly and the F/H/B looked askance. Mr Halliday looked up questioningly from the whisky glasses he was setting out. 'Did I hear right?' asked the F/H/B looking across to Mr Wild. 'That you wants a sweet sherry, same as yer missus?' 'Well, we don't often take alcohol, like, and I'm none too sure...' He hesitated.

''Ee'll hev whisky, same as us, if you please, Sir,' said the F/H/B to our host. ''Ee'll never be able to call hisself a proper Exmoor man on half a glass of sherry.'

'Four whiskies coming right up,' said Mr Halliday, handing round a treble apiece.

Mrs Halliday and I decided on dry Martinis, and we all sat sipping our drinks and gazing out through the great circular window at the lawns and terraces carved out of the cliffside. We clinked our glasses, drank to Wellington's long and happy retirement and watched the sun sink into the sea. Our glasses were recharged by our generous hosts and conversation ebbed and flowed over horses we had known then Seemingly recited a little poem about an old horse who died on his last hunt. Mr and Mrs Wild were enjoying themselves, if somewhat bemused. Mr Wild was doing so well on the whisky that somebody proposed a toast to 'Our new Exmoor man'. I eased up on my own intake as it looked like I might be the only driver left standing.

As darkness closed in I felt it was time to marshal the revellers into an orderly departure but they appeared as reluctant to depart as our hosts were to break up the party. A great dish of cheese and pickle sandwiches manifested themselves from somewhere and our visitors, normally a quiet, sedate couple, ate, drank and conversed with gusto. It was likely that Mr Wild's whisky intake and his wife's umpteenth sweet sherry had some bearing on it.

We finally bade our goodbyes, and made our way outside to the pig van, where Seemingly took his front passenger seat again and the F/H/B and other two passengers piled untidily on to the straw in the back. I fastened the back doors on them, climbed into the driver's seat and started up, steering carefully up the bumpy, unfamiliar lane. Behind me the F/H/B led the singing with 'Old MacDonald Had A Farm' and we all joined in the ee-i-ee-i-o bits.

Seemingly reckoned it was impossible to see with the pig van's poor lights and somewhere I took a wrong turning because we found ourselves passing a moorland pub, well out of our way. It was late, well after eleven, but the lights were on and Seemingly let out a bellow. 'Stop, missus, stop, I gotta see a chap about a dog!' He got out and unfastened the back doors to let out the passengers.

Mr and Mrs Wild were puzzled by this unscheduled stopover, saying that they had no need to get out and would wait in the van. Seemingly, backed by the F/H/B, would not hear of it and we all followed our leaders into the bar where they were greeted by the landlord like long-lost friends. Drinks were ordered and some time later I downed my third tomato juice and gathered my folks together for the last leg home. It was a fairish drive, and the revellers' spirits were decidely flagging by the time I pulled up outside Seemingly's cottage. I helped him out and into his kitchen, leaving him in his old armchair. Back home the F/H/B and the guests welcomed some assistance, in fact I escorted the Wilds upstairs to their bedroom where they sank heavily on to their bed, not looking either to the right or the left but just staring straight ahead.

Rusty, their dog, got out from his basket and wagged his tail at them but it seemed unlikely that he would get his usual run out unless I took him myself. He followed me down to the yard and in the moonlight I was surprised to see F/H/B still there. He was standing next to the old water trough with the sleeves of his woollen cardigan rolled up to his elbows and his arms plunged painfully into a bunch of stinging nettles growing out of the wall, repeating 'Oh Christ, oh Christ,' over and over.

I led him indoors to bed, and by six in the morning he was up and about, with severe nettlerash on his arms, but with no recollection of how it came about.

At eight o'clock, as usual, I tapped at the odd looking blue humps on their pillows, which turned out to be Mr and Mrs Wild, fully dressed and still wearing their lookalike blue anoraks from the night before. They were pale and declined breakfast, saying they preferred to stay in bed. I took Rusty out again, who, by this time must have wondered just what was going on.

We ate our breakfast, and I was smoothing comfrey ointment into the F/H/B's arms, when Seemingly turned up, his usually ruddy face pale and unshaven.

''I bin riding a hoss all bleddy night,' he told us.

The F/H/B cackled unsympathetically. 'You means you bin dreaming? I ain't surprised, us got two more upstairs that don't know if 'tis Christmas or Easter.'

'I means jus' what I told 'ee,' corrected Seemingly irritably.

'I bin riding the bleddy porcelain hoss, back home. Blest if I know what got into me guts, but summat did. 'Tweren't as if us had ort unusual to drink, I jus' dunno.'

There was a knock on the door and Mr Wild came into the kitchen, still wearing his blue anorak and waggling a finger at the three of us. 'Don't you ever,' he said, 'don't you ever, ever ask us to go with you again to buy a horse.'

The need never arose, for within a week we had a message from a lady horse dealer who was certain she had the right pony to suit us. Unaccompanied, this time, the two of us set off to consider this latest offering, and, as soon as the bright little five-year-old chestnut was led out, I knew that, barring severe misbehaviour, this had to be the one.

The little mare was genuine, and was offered on a week's free trial. The price was more than we intended to pay but the lady dealer was adamant in not being beaten down. The deal was finally clinched with the F/H/B settling for the asking price, but to include the head-collar the pony was wearing, free delivery and a bottle of Grouse for luck.

Chapter Eight

I once read a newspaper account of a farmer's wife in Cumbria who was up a stepladder whitewashing her kitchen ceiling when through the window she noticed her husband and son in the yard loading sheep into a lorry and from the shouting, swearing and barking dogs gathered things were not going quite accordingly. Deciding to lend a hand, she left her brush and bucket of whitewash on top of the stepladder, climbed down, jumped into her welly boots and slipped out through the back door, not bothering to close it.

In the yard she found all the sheep had been loaded except one, and that was the animal causing all the commotion, dodging hither and thither, anywhere but up the ramp into the lorry. The game little woman joined in the chase, then, to her dismay, the sheep veered out of the yard, up the garden path, through the open door and into the kitchen. Her worst fears were confirmed as she pounded behind it, seconds too late to stop the almighty crash as the sheep collided with the stepladder and the bucket of whitewash emptied over its woolly coat like a missile direct on target. Away it went on a mad jaunt around the house, whitewashing walls, furniture, armchairs, curtains, up the stairs and down, before it was finally ambushed behind the hat-stand and heaved out through the front door.

The farmer's wife then spent the rest of the day and all night scrubbing whitewash off the furniture and carpets, and washing curtains and covers. Her story reached the press and resulted in a newspaper interview, with the reporter asking how she felt after having her home whitewashed by a sheep. Stoically, she answered, 'Oh, it was just one of them little misfortunes that can happen to anybody!' and, nodding proudly, 'not a penny claimed off insurance!'

I was so impressed by this stout Cumbrian lady that I read the story aloud to the F/H/B one dinnertime.

'What a plucky little woman,' I finished, folding the newspaper.

'Huh,' he said, shovelling down dinner like a tractor taking on fuel.

'What's "huh" s'posed to mean?' I asked.

'Well, 'twas 'er own fault, weren't it?'

This was unjust. 'How can you say such a thing. 'Twas accidental. The sheep got in through the back door.'

'Aye. And who left this door open? 'Er did.'

'But only 'cos she went to help.'

'Interfere,' corrected the F/H/B. 'Who asked her to go out there in the fust place? Nobody. If 'er had stopped up that ladder and minded 'er business, none of it woulda happened.'

'But she went to lend a hand.'

'Nobody asked 'er to do ort,' persisted the F/H/B. 'Interfering woman, that's what 'er was. Shoulda keeped up that ladder wi' 'er whitewash.'

He pushed his empty dinner plate away and picked up his dessert spoon impatiently. 'Where's me pudden?' he demanded. 'I come in here to eat me dinner, not listen to you yanging on 'bout some mazed ol' up-country woman rinning arter a sheep.'

This conversation reminded me of the thin dividing line between what is considered 'helping' on a farm, and what is classed as 'interfering'. A farmer's wife can be 'helping' when summoned to the yard just because Farmer needs somebody to silently stand there to be sworn at, whereas if she stands there and proffers advice she can be accused of interfering and curtly ordered back indoors. Most of us, like the Cumbrian lady, manage to shrug off our little misfortunes although it would be imprudent, to say the least, to stand there happily smiling whilst a torrent of abuse is being hurled at us. Our features are grievously composed whilst our minds race over what's for dinner, is that hen over there behind the tractor scratching out a nest, and what funny ways farmers have of showing their love. We all know it's there all right but it is no good day-dreaming to the extent that you bungle the dismissive 'you can be off, now', which gets you five more minutes lecturing for not paying attention.

This haranguing is acceptable amongst men and women who work the soil and is certainly not confined to the peasant farmer. Perhaps they feel free in the wide open spaces to give vent to their feelings without the niceties of decorum expected in a more urban society.

One of our neighbours was an old Etonian who owned a farm about a mile across the fields from us and now and again we would see him in the local pub with his arm draped lovingly across the shoulders of his pleasant little wife, intoning, 'Bottoms up, darling, and have another drinkie.' Then, the next day, very likely, and only if the wind was in the right direction, we would hear his voice berating her when they shifted their cattle. 'Stop those bloody bullocks – STOP them, I say – oh, Christ, look what you've done, now they're on their way to bloody Dulverton and it's all your sod-assing fault. You're a bloody misfit, that's what you are!'

The F/H/B and I would unashamedly hang on every word, not daring even to whisper in case we missed the grand finale. We were rarely disappointed. The air would be rent with the little wife's great wracking sobs, overlapped with the cultured tones from England's most famous public school. 'That's right – snivel. That's all you're bloody fit for, snivelling. What have I had with you? Ten years of bloody misery, that's what, and now you've let the buggering bullocks go to Dulverton! Christ Almighty!' The sobs would fade into the distance as the unfortunate pair trudged off to the village in search of their errant cattle and a big smile would spread over the F/H/B's face as his eyes met mine and he grinned, 'Do have another drinkie, darling!'

I felt sorry for the poor woman, as did all the neighbouring wives, for making the mistake of collapsing in tears. Farming toughens women. Everyday problems must be tackled and mastered and even if we do not always enjoy it, at least it becomes bearable and we learn to overcome any little misfortunes.

A number of these, if not actually precipitated by the livestock, take place in the farmyard, which, by nature of its design and use, make it a high-risk area. Fortunately, the summer visitors rarely viewed it that way, in fact, with their car parked up, they seemed to look on it like an oasis in the desert, a safe place from which they could make daily sorties to the outside world and return each evening to be fed and watered. The teeming farmyard life was viewed magnanimously, as though everything must be friendly because it was in the country, from cats' muddy paw marks across a polished car bonnet, to the coo-ing, circling doves, thoughtfully eyeing uncovered tourists as they strolled trustingly across the forecourt. Wandering, itchy cows, looking for a scratching post, could flatten a car door in seconds then turn round and do the other side before ambling off, still rhythmically chewing their cud and swishing their tails without as much as a backward glance at the scrunched-up vehicle. Towering over everything was that old farmyard standard, the dung heap.

Thus was the scene set for the arrival of Mr and Mrs Devlin, their four children and an aunt, who had booked a week's holiday in April, commencing on a Friday. A few days before their arrival Mr Devlin telephoned to ensure there would be suitable parking for his Rolls Royce. No specific mention had been made about his car in the original booking, which was not unusual as it seemed obvious that it would be impractical to visit a remote farm without some form of transport. And although there was a small garage across the yard, it was requisitioned in spring for ewes and lambs, along with all the other outhouses. I assured the owner there was plenty of space in the yard for his car but as I slowly replaced the phone I was filled with trepidation. A Rolls. And four children. And an auntie. They had to be millionaires. The house suddenly looked old and shabby and the yard, dominated by the dung heap – at its most massive in the springtime and embellished with the odd clump of stinging nettles here and there – looked as if it would have benefited from a stick of dynamite.

Howsoever, my fears were allayed on the Friday when the Devlin family eased their gleaming black limousine into the yard. The Rolls was a hearse. They were not millionaires. Mr Devlin turned out to be an undertaker from Bournemouth and had crammed all the family, even Auntie Gladys, who was their embalmer, into their business vehicle for their holiday on Exmoor.

The funeral director was a tall, distinguished looking man with greying 'sideboards' and a courteous manner, a presence that would lend decorum to a sacred occasion. I noticed most of his conversation was not addressed directly to his wife, or children, or Auntie Gladys, but to the Lord above. Possibly it had something to do with his calling although somehow he never struck me as being a particularly religious man, in fact some of his supplications bordered on the downright blasphemous. His hearse was his greatest pride. He told us it had been thoroughly overhauled and serviced the previous week. '£1800 that cost me,' he confided, patting the gleaming body-work fondly. 'And then when I collected her from the garage you'll never believe what happened as I drove out.' 'Oh, no, not an accident?' I queried, appalled. Mr Devlin shook his fine head almost disbelievingly, as though recalling a nigh unbearable memory, then rolled his eyes heavenwards and spread his hands in a gesture almost of reproach.

'It rained,' he said dramatically. 'Oh, my dear God, all that money, and it rained first time out.'

Fortunately, the Bournemouth family had picked a fine week, so there seemed little fear of rain spots spattering their magnificent limousine. At the beginning they all piled into it for a number of enjoyable outings but, as Mr Devlin put it, the Exmoor scenery soon paled compared to the delights of our trout pond at the bottom of the orchard. All the family had rods and fishing tackle, and anticipating

returning home with a fine catch, had requested that I stored ice
packs for their cool bags in the farm freezer.

They were a charming family and marvellously good company,
with a fund of tombstone humour, particularly Auntie Gladys who
was a little bird-sharp Welsh lady with thinning red hair, a gleeful
cackle, and a fondness for stout, bottles of which she carried everywhere in an old tapestry holdall. 'I gave up embalming years ago,
see,' she told us in her lilting accent. 'But I only stuck it for a week –
I missed the company!'

Mrs Devlin, a quieter woman with sympathetic brown eyes and an
abundance of dark hair curling softly round her almost-pretty face,
obviously worried about Auntie Gladys sinking too many stouts, with
her stories getting saltier by the bottle. She would attempt to curb the
flamboyant old lady in the evening by looking up from her knitting and
saying quietly, and with just a hint of disapproval, 'Don't you think it's
time you got off to bed, Auntie?' To which the embalmer would reply
with a little screech, 'Bed? You bloody die in bed and I ought to know
about that, now don't I?' And with one swift movement she would
forage in the tapestry bag and out would come another bottle of forti-
fying stout, a hefty slurp, and Auntie would swing back into her stride
again, her Welsh accent even more pronounced.

'Now, my ducks, have you heard the one about...' Her fund of
stories was never-ending, and we made an appreciative audience, the
F/H/B thwacking his knees and rocking with laughter long before
the punch line was delivered, spluttering ''Tis the way 'er tells 'em!'
When finally she picked up her bag and headed for bed, her cackle
fading in the distance, Mr Devlin would put his finger-tips together
and murmur devoutly, 'Thank you, Christ, for that,' and Mrs Devlin
laid aside her knitting and visibly relaxed.

The family were all earlybirds in the morning, out and about in the
yard long before breakfast, and taking an active interest in the farmyard activities. The four children aged from about six to fifteen, were
polite and well-mannered and the F/H/B was delighted to have
them helping, and tutoring each one on milking the house cow. Their
father lovingly polished his hearse, and Mother and Auntie Gladys
searched for hens' nests in the straw barn, the former emerging
looking as calm and immaculate as when she went in, and Auntie
with straw in her hair, pop-eyed with enthusiasm. 'You'd never
believe the effort that those dear little chickens put into laying just
one little egg!'

After filling up on their farmhouse breakfast, they would collect their picnic for the day and all leave the yard in a little straggling procession, with Mother and Father leading, then the children, all with their rods and lines, trailed by Auntie Gladys, hugging her tapestry bag, en route for the trout pond and the little River Brocky that ran through the valley. They were followed, more often than not, by two or three of the farm cats, all fishing enthusiasts, and Skipper the old sheepdog, enjoying his retirement and free to relax as he pleased.

Before they returned in the late afternoon, I would check on their car but the nearest it came to being vandalised were the inevitable cats' paw prints daubed across the pristine bonnet. I rubbed at them with a finger but that just spread them around so I dusted to and fro with the sleeve of my jumper, with more success.

At teatime they all toiled back up the hill, still carrying their empty bags, but never disheartened, always cheerfully looking forward to 'another day tomorrow', although as the week wore on without any catch I fancied there was a certain anxiety over their lack of success. The F/H/B sensed the children's disappointment and told them there would be a 50p reward for whoever caught the biggest fish.

The anxiety I originally felt over the liability of the Rolls standing for long daylight hours in the yard, began to fade as days came and went, with the hearse and our pig wagon parked safely and companionably side-by-side, sharing the cats and specks of dust, but otherwise not much happening.

On the visitors' last night Auntie Gladys rattled off roughly a joke a minute, cackling like a demented chicken and going into lengthy explanations to ensure none of us missed the punch line. 'Here's one about a helicopter pilot and a postmistress with a wooden leg ...' and finishing with 'by helicopter... get it, my loveys? By hell-he-copped her!' Mrs Devlin lowered her eyes and took a sudden fierce interest in her knitting and her husband pleaded 'Oh, dear God, no, not another one!' as the little embalmer waved a fresh bottle of stout aloft and cried, 'Yoo-hoo! Here goes nothing! Now let me tell you about this constipated nun on her way to the Chemist...'

It was one o'clock in the morning before Auntie Gladys was finally heaved up the stairs to bed but the next day all the family were in the yard before breakfast, with the undertaker painstakingly polishing his car. They planned to leave in the afternoon after a couple of hours' fishing in a last effort to catch the trout that had eluded them all week.

After breakfast I wished them luck as they set off down the valley, then I quickly cleared the dishes before going upstairs to change the beds in readiness for the next guests. I had almost finished when there was the roar of a powerful tractor engine in the yard, ten times the decibels of our own wheezing machine. I finished laying out towels and soap in the four-poster room, then crossed to the window where I could see a gigantic Fordson Major tractor with a fore-loader on the front and a muck spreader hitched to the back, purposefully chugging across the yard towards the dung heap. Steering it was Speedy, who was the nearest we ever got to an agricultural contractor, bent on honouring his annual spring muck-spreading contract. It was the end of April and the time was right to shift the unsightly muck heap from the yard and spread it across the cow field. Speedy needed no reminders, taking great pride in what he called 'Me h'agricultural contractions'.

Even this sounded too grand a title for what the F/H/B called a straightforward shit-carter with no trimmings. There were no written agreements, no printed bill-heads, no hourly rate, no time worked, no fuel consumption, no anything, not even a bill on a scrap of paper. Just once every year, Speedy dressed in his best suit, best shirt, collar and stagshead tie, presented himself in the kitchen, chaired a prolonged debate on farming, and finally reached deep into his jacket pocket for a small water-stained notebook which he would hold at arm's length across the table, squinting at the pages as he turned them, until he came across our name pencilled in with the amount we owed for twelve months' contractions. Nothing else. 'Pound notes, Squire, if you'd be so good,' he would say, snapping shut his little notebook and turning his full attention to the tankard of beer the F/H/B set before him.

Besides his tractor, Speedy owned an ancient cattle transporter, which, like its owner, appeared to run on best bitter, getting slower and thirstier as the day wore on. It worked very well for the lucky ones, first in the queue in the a.m. with their sheep and bullocks at market but going into a decline in the p.m.

Everybody knew that Speedy's deadline was no later than six o'clock, and after that his whereabouts was anybody's guess, whether he had a load up or not. We waited up one wet and blustery night in October until after midnight for his lorry to come lurching down the lane like a speeded-up version of the Keystone Kops. As he turned into our yard the F/H/B ordered, 'Git yer boots on, Maid,' anticipating that all hands would be needed to unload the sheep in the dark.

He was right. The wind howled around the inky blackness of the night, the rain beat down relentlessly, and when the ramp was lowered the sheep unanimously decided they were better off inside than outside. We got them moving eventually, but being sheep, they went from downright refusal to jet propelled, running riot across the yard, anywhere but through the open gate to their field. Speedy flapped his arms inside his tattered raincoat and sang cheerfully throughout, 'Ho, I wish I wuz down on the farm.' The F/H/B blinked through the blackness for bleating sheep and roared, 'You carry on like this once more, Speedy Draper, and you won't be down on this bleddy farm no more. Not never!' He took off his sodden cap, wrung it out with both hands and replaced it on his head before slamming up the ramp and ordering me, well within Speedy's earshot, to 'Make sure you shut the gate after that mazed bugger, Maid,' thus dismissing our Drover without the hot toddy he would have expected on such a night. He stopped singing as he climbed into his lorry, whilst the F/H/B squelched off to the field with a torch to check on the sheep.

Howsoever, Speedy was such a warm character that no one could take offence for long with him, and although younger and classier contractors started up, they seemed to come and go, whilst his ramshackle little business ticked busily on.

On this particular April day, with the great tractor chugging across the yard, my first thought was for the gleaming limousine, still parked next to the pig van, and some distance from the muck heap. I all but fell down the stairs in my rush to the yard, running and shouting above the roar of the tractor and pointing frantically to the hearse. 'Careful how you go!'

Speedy's big, round face grinned down at me from a great height, and he adjusted his cap from front to back in acknowledgment.

'I'll look arter'n like 'ees there fer me own funeral!' he vowed in stentorian tones. He righted his cap and drove the foreloader into the dung. It was good and juicy, with pungent steam rising in little eddies. I turned back to the house.

Some time later I heard the tractor reverse across the yard, and then stop. Speedy's voice bawled, 'Missus! Yer a minute.' I darted out the nearest door, the front one, still wearing my house shoes, aware that any sort of accident could have happened, farmyards and farm tractors are fearsome combinations.

Speedy was all right, he was walking towards me. Speedy was speaking. 'Buggered if I knows 'ow it 'appened, missus, I only shoved the bleddy thing in reverse and next minute there's shit flying all abroad, and there's your ol' van and thik other one sticked right out backside on, and, well, I dunno', they just catched the tail end o' it.'

I shot past him, skidding through the muck in my thin shoes, concerned only with the visitors' property; the pig van mattered not at all. If it had not been for their different sizes they would have been indistinguishable. As it was, they looked like mother and child, little and large, both pasted with cow dung with a little criss-cross of straw here and there, as though to break up the pattern. What was it the Cumbrian lady said about smiling at life's little misfortunes – I did more than that, I broke into wild laughter.

Speedy joined in. ''Tis only the frontsides of 'em,' he gasped between guffaws. 'Nort that a bucket of water won't do away wi'. Bleddy ol' muck spreader,' he went on thoughtfully. 'Never went right from the minute I pulled in, 'twas like 'ee wuz constipated, so I gived'n a thump wi' a 'ammer and BANG, out it all flied like a bullock that ain't shat fer a fortnight.'

'Get the broom,' I ordered, 'and I'll look for the hosepipe.' I feared that all too soon the family were likely to return from their fishing trip and it was hard to visualize Mr Devlin joining in the merriment when he spotted his hearse under its steamy camouflage. Neither, I fancied, would the F/H/B, who was mercifully out of the way, shifting sheep and mending gaps in fences.

Ignoring the pig van, we broomed and hosed the big car, all the while glancing anxiously over our shoulders towards the gateway, like a couple of criminals giving their getaway car the full treatment.

''Tis master good luck, that stuff,' maintained Speedy as he prised at the elegant radiator, and scarcely were the words out of his mouth than old Skipper plodded through the gateway, followed by a couple of ginger cats. Time had run out. The fishing party was back. As I stood back to survey the dripping motor the family followed the animals into the yard, trooping over to us, laughing and waving and shouting with excitement, all talking at once.

'I've won the 50p,' piped the smallest boy, ''cos I caught the biggest fish.'

'Mine's bigger than yours,' disputed his sister.

'Trout, glorious trout,' sang a flushed Auntie Gladys.

Mr Devlin fumbled with his green fishing bag, wrenching it open to reveal half a dozen fresh, gleaming trout. 'Success, success,' he beamed. 'Our very last day, and by Christ Almighty, we've done it.'

'I expect it's our lucky day,' smiled his wife.

'There now,' interrupted Speedy, looking me straight in the eye. 'Wot did I tell 'ee 'bout luck?'

Mr Devlin leaned across his car and flicked a small lump of something from a headlamp.

I tried an explanation. 'Our friend here…' indicating Speedy. 'Our friend has had a slight mishap with the manure spreader. Our pig van got in the way, and with your car being next to it, we sort of thought if we just hosed a drop of water over it.'

I was floundering when I realised nobody was paying the slightest attention to a word I was saying. They were grouped, as if mesmerised, round the fish bag, gazing at their day's catch.

I went indoors and made sandwiches and coffee for the departing guests and the family eventually climbed in their hearse and drove off to Bournemouth. I thought it looked fairly presentable but Speedy voiced doubts. ''Tis funny stuff, that old cow shat,' he mused. 'Years agone they used to paste it on ceilings. Made 'em waterproof.' 'Why should they want waterproof ceilings?' I wondered. 'Well,' Speedy patiently explained, 'back in they days privies was down the bottom of the garden, so they all had piss-pots, in their bedrooms. Then they'd git a bit cidered-up and come the middle o' the night they'd fall outa bed in the dark, miss the piss-pot, and Bob's yer uncle, and there 'twas all over the danged floor and drip, drip through the ceiling. So, they pasted cow shat on the ceiling underneath to waterproof'n. Sometimes they distempered over'n, sometimes they didn't, so there was a lot of browny coloured ceilings about. If there was any shine on'n 'afore, a lick of cow shat took it clean off. 'Tis acid. Now I wouldn't mind betting there won't be a helluva shine on thik hearse tomorrow, nor on your ol' pig van, either, come to think o'it. Not that 'ee matters a lot, but that hearse, well, I dunno'.' Speedy's soliloquy trailed off as we set to work on the pig van. Sadly, we never heard from our jolly undertaker again.

Chapter Nine

Once upon a time there lived on Exmoor a handsome young shepherd boy of some nineteen summers who was happy and content to tend his sheep – and had ventured no farther than ten miles to the north, south, east and west of the moor. Far away, in a big city, there lived a glamorous, dark-haired, blue-eyed career woman of some thirty summers who was also happy and contented and engaged to be married to a high-flying executive who worked for a world-famous firm of motor manufacturers. He had no time for holidays, so friends of the career girl took her away from the hustle and bustle of the life she loved, to their secret hideaway at Chilcott Farm, where she made a spectacular entrance in a floaty designer dress and a cloud of Miss Dior. Her friends took her to the village stores and fitted her out with stout jumpers and corduroys and wellington boots and she tackled steak and kidney pie dinners and junket and cream, and the F/H/B thought it a shade unnatural to turn a silk purse into a sow's ear.

Then her friends decided it was time to introduce her to the locals and took her one evening to the local cider hostelry and, as she stepped through the door, tall and lovely, heads bent low over the local brew were raised and an almost audible sigh rippled through the Public Bar, and the little blonde shepherd boy in from the hills, turned to gaze enraptured at the vision. Their eyes met, locked, and stayed that way. It was love at first sight.

They wed six months later in the local church and the bride was sophisticated and beautiful in palest beige and carried freesias, and the little shepherd boy, now nearly twenty, wore a grown-up suit with a white carnation buttonhole. Eighteen months later it was all over. The bride set off, sad and alone, on a round-the-world trip that was to last three years, and the bridegroom took up with a dairymaid from Porlock. End of Fairy Tale. Marriages are not always made in Heaven, neither were they made at Chilcott.

Perhaps it was all too fast and furious. It might well work out in towns but hereabouts everything is taken at a more cautious pace. The courting period is statutory – you winter them, summer them, then winter them again, and by then you should have both made up your mind one way or the other.

Town maidens are often so unacquainted with rural etiquette that even commencing a conversation with a countryman can be a hit-or-miss affair. I recall June, one of our more seductive guests, blonde, saucer-eyed, tight trousers and three husbands to her credit, meeting Seemingly, our bachelor neighbour.

'Hi, Handsome,' she coo-ed, to which his gruff reply was simply 'You got a husband!'

'Three, actually,' she purred, somewhat non-plussed at Seemingly's speedy rejection. This opening had obviously brought success else-where, but whereas in a town it would probably be smiled at as merely flirtatious, encouraged even, in the country it would be regarded as 'horsing', not a flattering predicament for a lady to be in. Not unless she's a mare in season and can't help it.

Our country men are without guile, women take them as they are, or not at all. Women's Lib is despised, they refuse to acknowledge that any woman, anywhere, would ever be permitted to burn her Welly boots. Their attitude is firmly Victorian and to be influenced in any way by a woman is considered sissy.

The F/H/B poked fun unmercifully at Nigel, a very eligible bach-elor who spent most of his holidays at Chilcott and was heavily under the influence of every new girlfriend he brought with him. 'If it weren't for your wife's cooking I wouldn't come here to be insulted,' he told the F/H/B, who responded with 'Please your bleddy self' accompanied with a pitying look as he reached for the whisky bottle. 'Now then, my lad, you just hev a coupla noggins o' this and go upstairs and tell 'er who's boss.'

'Ho, yes, indeed, rather,' enthused Nigel but his new-found courage faded overnight, because the next morning, when I took in their tea, there he was, sitting up in bed with his then girlfriend's two labradors and a pile of doggie magazines. I remembered that his previous girlfriend had been a sailing enthusiast and he had looked quite dashing wearing a yachting cap at a jaunty angle, which he hung on the bed-post overnight, as though he could not bear to be parted from it. The F/H/B thought differently, more like it was there to remind him which lady he was waking up next to in the morning.

Nigel had no chosen sport of his own, other than a bit of half-hearted jogging which gave him carte blanche to dress in a fancy leisure outfit and expensive trainers. He never did things by halves, whichever sport he was following at the time got the full treatment. This year it was the World of Dogs. Sporting Dogs. Every day was geared to Giving the Dogs a Good Holiday, and Nigel and the girlfriend relentlessly tramped the moors in all weathers wearing Barbours (genuine, of course, no cheap imitations) and big brimmed hats and carrying thumb-sticks. They would return exhausted but after a bath and a hearty dinner the young man would deck himself out in his turquoise jogging outfit and run the three miles to the pub in Dulverton. The girlfriend and the dogs drove down in the car and picked him up at closing time. This routine worked very well until one night towards the end of their holiday, when the young lady thought her dogs might prefer to run home, and Nigel could go with them. 'But not on the road, darling, it's far too dangerous for them, you'll have to cut across the fields.' It was after closing time and only just daylight when he dutifully set off up the one-in-four hill before leaving the road and turning left down a steep field with a stream at the bottom. There was no foot-path to follow and once through the stream it was uphill all the way until he reached our own muddy lane which led to all the fields. It turned out to be an exceptionally dark, moonless night and we all waited up for Nigel's grand entrance after his marathon run. Midnight came and went, and the F/H/B was just organising a search party when the runner and two exhausted dogs fell through the front door into the cider room. All three were plastered in cow dung. Nigel eventually regained his breath and explained in great staccato bursts how darkness had set in and he had lost his way across the fields. He couldn't see the cow pats and kept falling in them, and obviously the same fate had befallen the dogs. He was upset. He was out of breath. His expensive white trainers were ruined. Whose tomfool idea was it in the first place? It was the end of yet another dream. The turquoise outfit, the trainers and the romance all ended up together in our dustbin.

The following year produced a new girlfriend, a tall and striking dark-haired beauty with a hint of knowingness about her eyes.

It was a hot afternoon when they arrived, and the F/H/B was in the kitchen drinking a glass of cider. The glass was halfway to his mouth when the young lady smouldered into the kitchen, but although his mouth opened, it stayed that way and the cider trickled down his shirt front unheeded. Her fantastic figure was covered from neck to toe in figure-hugging, sensuous black leather; Nigel had grown his hair into a fashionable new style and abandoned his ruddy, outdoor complexion for a pale and interesting look that seemed to match up with the black leather gear he was wearing.

The Black Beauty was introduced as Olwyn as we all settled down to a glass of cider together, and the F/H/B recovered his composure enough to engage her in conversation.

'What do you do for a living, me dear?' he asked.

She was ruthlessly forthright, tossing back her long hair from her face.

'I'm a pornographic model,' she answered simply.

Even the F/H/B had no answer to that, other than a weak, 'Well done!' which is an old Westcountry standby for when you're struck dumb, and can be uttered with varying inflexions, from a praiseworthy 'WELL DONE!' when a local cricketer hits a six, to a sarcastic 'Well done' when somebody's out for a duck, to a feeble mouthing of the words when a lady announces she's a pornographic model.

We saw little of them for the rest of the week, other than at meal times. Nigel had abandoned his tramps through the heather along with his Barbour and floppy-brimmed hat, neither did he seem to read in bed, or even drink tea in the morning. They cancelled the tea as they thought I had enough to do without bothering with tea for them.

The other guests that week had little in common with Nigel and his Black Beauty, being a small party of people from Blackpool, one of whom was Chairman of the Bench. We had enjoyed their company for a number of years, finding them quietly amusing, high-principled people. The wife of the chairman was a chatty, easy-going little body, who could be relied on to keep the conversation round the dinner table from flagging, and she and the model seemed to chat together much of the time. Olwyn had long since abolished her black leather gear in favour of little floral print dresses, which gave her an air of pretty demureness. But whereas she smiled and conversed, giving the impression that she was enjoying the holiday, he turned unusually pale and silent, moody almost, which gave rise to speculation among the other guests and the F/H/B as to the reason for it. On their last morning she asked me if they could stay an extra day, which I affirmed, and resulted in her brief, but heavily loaded announcement in the dining room that evening. 'I've decided to stay another night, it's doing me so much good!' Adding, irrelevantly, 'After all, it is the strawberry-and-cream season.' The Chairman of the Bench could contain himself no longer. 'More like the rutting season!' he guffawed with a strangled cry, burying his face in his serviette, his shoulders heaving. The Model flashed her perfect teeth, unabashed, but Nigel stared mirthlessly down at his plate of steak and kidney pie, more like a man about to face a firing squad than an invitation to spend another night with a pornographic model.

After the couple's departure revelations came from the chairman's wife. 'Well, indeed,' she said, 'I have read about those sort of young people but I've never actually met one before. I mean, I felt I knew that young man's anatomy almost as well as she did. Didn't so much as lower her voice.' (Mrs Hall was whispering.) 'She said...' Mrs Hall was struggling with her words. 'She said five orgasms in one night and two in the afternoon. Make no wonder he looked poorly.' She pronounced the word orgasm as though uttering it for the first time ever. It probably was. People have different vocabularies according to the lives they lead.

Recounting this to the F/H/B, I recalled how demure the young lady had looked once she settled to a country holiday. He was sceptical. 'How many times hev I told 'ee, Maid, you don't judge a sausage by 'ees skin. You won't see that one again, you mark my words. The old boy'll turn up again, though, 'tis like a second home to 'ee.' Well not quite, I thought. It hardly seemed likely Nigel would have introduced his outspoken girlfriend to his own mother and father, who were respected pillars of their local Presbyterian Chapel and chaired meetings for unmarried mothers.

Nevertheless, the F/H/B was right on the first count. The following year Nigel was back and heavily into a new relationship, this time with another sporting lady, a horsey one. The bedroom was scattered with sports magazines, and when I took in the morning tea he was sitting up in bed requesting her to pass the *Horse and Hound*, darling, there's absolutely nothing in the *Shooting Times* this week.' And then, flicking through the pages with authority, 'Old Lester's in trouble already this season, I see.'

He was a townsman and this behaviour was unlikely to have happened with our country lads, who pander little to their womenfolk, engaging in a more 'take me as I am' attitude. Men are macho in these parts, they don't wear fancy braces with patterns, baler cord will do, and very often their flies are cobbled with baler cord, too. Non-matching, otherwise they might be considered effeminate.

Howsoever, most countrymen's intentions are strictly honourable and they look forward to leaving home and setting up in their own place with a wife to look after them, whereas townsmen are often more independent and take pleasure in living bachelor lives in their own property. They book double rooms for holidays with girlfriends with no more thought than booking a couple of bus tickets, whereas the ones who feel sinful are the middle-aged who invariably register as Mr and Mrs and are fearful of being found out. This is sometimes because, at that age, they are actually married, though not to one another. They are easily recognised, mainly because they lay a trail from the front door to the bedroom, commencing with the man carrying in all the heavy suitcases. At dinner he invariably produces a bottle of wine, usually red, and they both look at one another over their glasses and talk animatedly in low voices, but only to one another, they've no wish to include the landlady or other guests which might involve awkward questioning. They invariably decline early-morning tea.

The last couple I remember thus staying, added one more give-away, when, after retiring to the sitting room, the 'wife' immersed herself in a library book. Eventually the 'husband', touching her shoulder, tenderly asked, 'Enjoying your book, dear?' He genuinely meant it, and it was not mouthed between clenched teeth and did not mean, 'Will you put that damned book down for a minute and listen to what I've got to say?'

The biggest mistake made by such folk is to select a farm or small guest house in the first place. People are curious in small establishments. I'm curious, the F/H/B is curious, the other guests are curious. I would advise some vast emporium, such as the Holiday Inn at Plymouth, where they could mingle with the crowd. After all, they don't usually come for the scenery, anyway.

It is always noticeable how a relationship changes once a couple marry and lovers become husbands and wives. Jeff and Caroline were a jolly, country-loving couple from the Midlands, who holidayed with us for several years before they decided to marry. She had a sweet tooth and was inclined to over-indulge on desserts, which she piled high with clotted cream. After a few days the unaccustomed richness would take its toll and by the end of dinner she would begin to feel queasy and uncomfortable. Her boyfriend was sympathetic. 'Has my darling got a teeny-weeny pain in her tum-tum?' he would ask, before dashing upstairs to search for the Rennies. After they were married the conversation took on a different aspect. 'Ooh,' groaned Caroline after her second pudding and cream. 'My little tum-tum doesn't feel very well.'

'I'm not surprised,' said her husband, pouring himself another cup of coffee, 'considering the way you gollop your food.'

His wife was suffering and prepared to overlook the insult. 'Darling,' she said, hiccuping unbecomingly, 'just run upstairs and get my Rennies, will you?'

'Look,' he answered, 'you got legs the same as me. You got the guts-ache, you get the Rennies.'

The F/H/B came into the dining room in time to catch the last sentence. 'Spoken like an Exmoor man,' he said approvingly as Caroline hiccuped her way up the stairs. 'You start like you mean to go on, boy.' Caroline, luckily, was a great girl with a great sense of humour, and she learned to gently manipulate her husband. In future visits she confided that Jeff appeared to be something of a Jekyll and Hyde character. 'Quiet's a snail for eleven months of the year but likes to assert himself on holiday. Takes me a fortnight after we get home to gradually mould him back into shape again.' I laughed. 'You make him sound like a lump of plasticine.'

'Hmm, something like that,' she said thoughtfully.

◇◆◇

When it comes to romance, most country girls soon grasp that it is far more creditable to appear two eggs short of a dozen than two eggs over the top, knowing that the menfolk are cautioned from birth to beware of too intelligent women. They are lumped with too-intelligent pigs, and the fact is, you can't keep either in their sty, their brains tell them to go see what's in the Great Outside.

Once a young woman takes the initiative, it has to be done subtly, anybody flash rarely gets started. I am reminded of our attractive little widow woman visitor, Mrs Morgan, who, after sinking a couple of lunchtime sherries, seized the unsuspecting Pig Expert as he was searching up the road for missing bullocks. She dangled a sprig of mistletoe over his cap and pinned him against his own yard wall as he ducked and dodged the luscious lips seeking his, all the while gasping, 'You be bold, missus, you be bold!' before thrusting her to one side, hurriedly righting his cap, and charging out of reach as fast as his naily boots would take him.

A country girl is more likely to select her chosen man and bide her time until the right opportunity either presents itself or can be manoeuvred, for the attack. Market Day is as good as any, and after eyeing her man across the sheep pens, she might well follow up with a surefire conversation opener that brings an instant response. These are the three little words dear to every landowner's heart. 'How's your grass?' Grass is of such paramount importance that whole conversations are constructed around it, fortunes ebb and flow from the quality of grass; sheep and bullocks live and die from it. Farmers, struck dumb on other topical matters, expound articulately on their own grass, their neighbour's grass, and grass 'up country' (five miles to the north).

This is the sort of thing that makes it doubly difficult for outsiders to penetrate the system. Country folk, like Royalty, prefer their families to marry on the same level, it eliminates a few extra risks. What is more, mixed marriages between town and country require even more understanding between the participants than the conventional farmer's son/farmer's daughter alliance.

This was emphasized at close quarters when a North Country couple moved into the village with their only daughter. She turned out to be a particularly forward young woman in her twenties, who started off as she meant to go on, horsing around with several of the local lads, before setting her sights on a young farmer. As she was gaining a reputation as the local 'bicycle', his plans were immediate and did not encompass any permanent understanding. Her parents, however, having reached the stage where they could foresee problems arising from their daughter's diverse relationships, agreed that the unfortunate young man, if only a working farmer, might cut their losses in the event of a less favourable suitor.

The first we heard of the turn of events was when the young farmer slammed into our kitchen enraged. 'Whaddya think? That maid's father yanked me into their place last night and asked me what me intentions is. 'Tin as though her's even up the spout!'

'Git out quick,' the F/H/B advised, 'before 'tis too late.' But it was already too late and the next time the reluctant bridegroom appeared in the kitchen he brought the wedding present list. Two additional items of his own, a set of drain rods and roll of barbed wire, appeared in block capitals between the champagne flutes and the fondue set. He was swept up in elaborate preparations for the only daughter, culminating in a spring wedding with over a hundred guests, a vintage Rolls, champagne and a touching speech delivered by the bride's father in which he referred to his daughter as 'the only flower in our garden' which prompted an embarrassing stage whisper from the Best Man, 'Pity the frost never had her!'

Sadly, as forecast by the entire village, it all ended in tears. The bride did not take to the rigours of farming, and her mother was outraged when she discovered her daughter in the lambing shed carting buckets of water from the stream to fill numerous receptacles with drinking water for the sheep. She tackled her son-in-law about it, telling him that a trough and a tap in the shed would save his wife hauling water in buckets. He removed his cap for a second, scratched his head thoughtfully, then replied to his mother-in-law. 'So long's I got a woman, a bucket and a stream, I ain't spending no money on taps and troughs.' It was the beginning of the end, with the new wife finishing up serving in a shoe shop in Barnstaple and the husband tending his own sheep, an arrangement which suited everybody.

Matchmaking is a delicate operation to trifle with and all our efforts in that direction were doomed to failure. The couples that we tried to match never took off, fizzling out like damp squibs on their launching pad. Several eligible young bachelors spent their holidays with us, and, correspondingly, there were eight or nine young women that we watched grow up, and looked on as 'our girls'. Most of them matched themselves with partners from their own area, which was just as hit or miss as our own botched efforts on their behalf.

One of the most successful marriages was between a couple who were both first-time visitors to Chilcott. They each came on holiday with friends and chemistry took over as soon as they clapped eyes on one another. They both had a lot going for them, she being a spirited divorced lady, and he an Irishman with plenty of blarney. They kept in touch after the holiday and within weeks were back at the farm for a second meeting, two single rooms being booked, but this time the old floorboards along the passage were creaking around one in the morning, so everybody in the place knew which night the new friendship was consummated. Old-timers would have known there was only one way to creep that passage, and that was to straddle it with one leg against each wall, and then proceed like Wyatt Earp after a day riding the range. It was also necessary to check it was the right room on a dark night, as there were no locks on the doors, just old-fashioned latches.

Our romantic Irishman quickly announced their engagement, and, sentimentally, told us they planned to marry twelve months to the day that they first met at Chilcott. They did – and parted the same day. We heard afterwards that they spent the night before the wedding discussing calling the whole thing off, but decided they had left it too late since all the arrangements were made for a lavish ceremony. Their honeymoon was to be touring the Continent in their car, but they commenced a quarrel on the cross-Channel ferry which culminated in the bride emptying a pint of beer over her groom's head. He drove off at speed in France, leaving her with their passports but no return ticket. There was nothing for it but for her to stay alone in the hotel booked for their first night. He was later arrested at the German border for trying to cross without a passport and clapped in jail. Several days after they were reunited and the bridegroom decided it would be best to forget the disastrous Continental tour and return to England. They were travelling in their car with all their luggage when he turned for the dockside, but the bride thought not, although the one thing she did agree on was that up to then the honeymoon had hardly been a laugh a minute. She felt cheated; how many brides spend their wedding night alone in a foreign hotel without any money? She intended to have a honeymoon, with him or without him, he could suit himself. She shot out of the car door and disappeared, running up a side street, hotly pursued by her husband. The bride fled through the first open door she came across, which turned out to be a little machine factory, where a mad chase ensued, with the bridegroom, the foreman and a couple of workmen all dodging round the machinery after the fleeing honeymooner, who was screaming 'Police! Villains! Robbers! Kidnappers!' She was eventually caught and taken by taxi to the local hospital to be tranquillized before being shipped to England. Amazingly, they settled their differences and stayed together, learned to compromise, and settled into a successful a marriage. Which is some sort of achievement in this day and age when marriages are falling like ninepins.

I can pinpoint the commencement of marriage break-ups to the early 1970s. It started with long-standing visitors, an elegant couple with four children who wrote to tell us they were swopping partners with their next-door neighbours and we were not to get upset over it as they would all be marrying and everything would soon be back to normal.

In spite of the reassuring tone of the letter we were upset and the inquest lasted far into the night.

'Who would have thought it?'

'Well, they did argue a lot.'

'Everybody argues – look at us.'

'Wonder who'll get the dog?'

'Trust you to be more concerned about the bleddy dog than the kids.'

'You clouted two of 'em the last time they come.'

'I clout 'em every time they come and I don't doubt I'll do it again, if they ever comes back, that is.'

But come back they did, plus a bonus of two extra, because the new partners also had children. But we gasped at the first glimpse of the new wife, thinking it was, after all, the old one who had grown about six inches. Apart from the height difference, they would have passed for twin sisters. She was as charming, too, but perhaps she was too like the first wife, because one Christmas I received a sad little note from the children that told us, 'Our step-mum's left Dad and run off with our real mum's brother-in-law!' It was all too involved for our hillbilly minds to work out.

About this time, we had a similar telephone call from Bob, who was a travel agent with a business in Berkshire. He and his wife June used to jet off on exotic trips abroad, then come back to unwind at Chilcott, though I always thought 'unwind' an understatement for what took place when Bob hit the countryside. In one morning he would shear a sheep, ride the pony, catch a trout, and, if there was still time before lunch, seize the F/H/B's gun and shoot a rabbit. In the afternoon he would do it all over again, whilst June, all the while, relaxed sensibly in the garden. It was an amicable arrangement, as, I imagined, was the rest of their life, so news of their marriage break-up filled us with dismay. The news came in a telephone call from Bob. His wife, he told us, had left him; what was more, she had taken their only pet, a goldfish in a bowl. 'I really miss that little fish,' he said mournfully.

It was during our night-time inquest that we thought we might play Cupid and reconcile the warring partners. We made several pleading telephone calls to them both (June was at her mother's) and managed to get them to agree to a lunchtime meeting at a London restaurant, which, we reckoned, could be the first step towards a reconciliation. That night we had an outraged phone call from Bob, telling us that she had ordered all the dearest items on the menu, which was just what she would do, wouldn't she; it had cost an arm and a leg, thank God he was well rid of her. We learnt from that to keep clear of domestic disputes.

Some months later Bob asked if he might bring his new girlfriend to spend a week with us. We felt resentful at him replacing June with a newer model but when we first sighted her getting out of the car we thought there had been a reconciliation and June had switched from blonde to brunette. It took a full minute for it to register that this was indeed the newer, younger model, but with her predecessor's features. She, too, was charming and turned into a capable wife and mother.

Before long, June requested a booking for herself and her new boyfriend, who turned out to be a handsome policeman, and a very well-matched couple they looked, but it was not to be. They set up house together, but the romance was scuttled by the goldfish who lived on ants' eggs purchased by the policeman from a nearby pet shop which was run by a buxom redhead... He brought her down to the farm for a holiday. Love's roundabout was shuffling around at Chilcott at quite a pace. It did us no harm at all. The policeman had two children from his previous marriage; the redhead also had two children. Business was booming, doubled, if not trebled, at a stroke.

In years to come it seems doubtful that few will ever attain the goals set by society in more stable times. How many couples are likely to achieve their silver wedding anniversary, leave alone their pearl and ruby. Sticking together through thick and thin is laughed out of existence; who is right, who is wrong? An elderly Dutch couple staying with us mentioned they had just passed their fiftieth wedding anniversary. We were impressed. 'A Golden Wedding! How did you celebrate?' The husband looked down at the book he was reading, his wife did the talking. 'We had nothing to celebrate. The marriage has not been a great success,' was her stiff comment.

We still celebrate plenty of anniversaries in this area but then we celebrate anything and everything on Exmoor, the more the merrier. And farmers often have different thoughts from other human beings on what constitutes a celebration. I know one who took his wife on a surprise visit to Cutcombe Sheep Sales to commemorate their silver wedding. I count myself lucky that this was not my fate. Our Twenty-fifth fell on a Saturday and I could have been landed with Taunton Cattle Market, but the F/H/B showed he had a romantic side to his nature. To start with, he banned guests for that day, so that we were alone. Then he presented me with a dozen long-stemmed red roses, which was so romantic I nearly cried. In the afternoon he had planned for our neighbours, Tom and Gill, to pick us up in their car for a trip to the Torrington Farmers Point-to-Point races, which would be a treat for all of us. Then he told me, he had arranged what he called a 'little dinner outing', together with his brother, George (our best man) and my two sisters-in-law (our bridesmaids), but the destination was a secret.

We all enjoyed a splendid afternoon's racing, although I can't recall winning any money, and at the finish we all piled back into Tom's car, he turned on the ignition, and nothing happened. Not a sound. It worried me not at all, as, after all, it would be of little consequence if we were late for our little dinner outing, it was only the family, and they were not likely to make a fuss. Tom looked a bundle of nerves, but what the heck, it was just a flat battery and somebody, some-where in that crowd, would surely have jump leads. They did, and we eventually got started, going from 0-90 mph in seconds. 'Slow down, Tom,' I begged. 'It won't make no odds at all if we'm a bit late and you said yourself you'm not going anywhere, so you got all night to see your horses.' The F/H/B was unusually quiet, he looked half asleep.

Our neighbours tipped us out at our back door as though they hadn't a minute to live, refusing to come in for a drink, which was a bit disappointing on this special day, driving off up the road as though pursued by a thousand demons. Nevertheless, it was late, and by the time the cow was milked and the chickens and dogs and cats fed, we only had seconds to change before our best man and bridesmaids arrived. The F/H/B was determined to maintain secrecy over our rendezvous, for no sooner were we heading for Dulverton than my sisters-in-law started to wrap a scarf round my eyes. I strived to quell a harrowing thought that this outing was to be at my least favourite place, where we would end up with a spoon-ful of rice on a lettuce leaf and a choc ice with a meringue crumbled over it, the bridegroom having left it too late to book at a more popular place.

We seemed to drive round in circles until I had no idea of direction, then the car finally stopped and I was led up some steps and through a door. A band started to play 'Congratulations', my blindfold was whipped away, and I was facing two long lines of cheering, familiar faces, including Tom and Gill, all our local friends and what looked like all the visitors we had ever met. At the back our local baker and his wife stood beside a long table crammed with food and a great iced cake, whilst another table was packed with gaily coloured parcels. The F/H/B had planned and organised a Surprise Party. Now I knew why Tom was in such a hurry to get home that evening, they had a lot of horses to attend to and a short time to do it in. And the F/H/B said later that he had not fallen asleep in the back of the car, he was praying, having instructed everyone to be in Brushford Village Hall – for that is where we were – before eight o'clock that night, and there they all were, dressed in their best, familiar faces beaming. I had saved to buy my husband an Omega watch, but it seemed paltry compared to his efforts on my behalf, almost like a long service award to a loyal worker.

It had indeed been a day to cherish forever, and how sad it will be if so many marriages last so little time that special wedding anniversaries will be the exception rather than the rule.

Chapter Ten

Our wedding invitations became too numerous to be honoured and business was never better, with guests honeymooning with us for the second time around, and others honeymooning first and getting married after, and yet more on trial runs which failed miserably. Some of the youngsters had holidayed with us from babies, and whilst there were several young men, there was also a little contingent of nine or ten girls, all within the same age bracket, that the F/H/B always singled out as *his girls*. He taught them all to milk the Jersey cow, count the sheep ('you counts their legs, me dear, then divides by four!'), feed the chickens, search for eggs in the hay barn, and ride the pony. If they fell off they had to get right back on again, and without any help. Every one turned into a first class rider. If he had time at night, or the weather was bad, he would join them for card games, and the sitting room would rock with merriment as the F/H/B invented new rules as they played, whilst brazenly cheating himself. All of these special girls eventually brought their serious boyfriends along for his inspection; a tour round the farm and a game of cards were all that was necessary before he summed up the newcomer. Rosemary brought Maki all the way from Greece, and though he spoke little English and the F/H/B had to shout at the top of his voice to try to make him understand, he met with instant approval. Jane brought Tim, there were Christine and Richard, Isabel and Andy, Fiona and Fred, all passed the test. Others did not. But whereas the girls were at an age when they considered they knew better than their parents, they treated the F/H/B's judgement as sacrosanct, resulting in one or two of the less wholesome individuals meeting with dismissal on returning home.

We attended as many weddings as we could, with more likelihood of us going in the winter than the summer. And only then if Dudley was available to live in the house and attend to the livestock. He would see to the sheep, and feed them if necessary, milk the Jersey cow, let the horses in and out and attend to their feed, and see to the cats and dogs and poultry. Being totally reliable, he was in great demand. After his eighty-eighth birthday he gave up milking and looking after horses, but still house-sat and looked after chickens and pets. He had a little red book in which he listed all his regular clients and their holiday dates, which seldom varied from year to year, and the rest of us he juggled around to the best of his ability. Sometimes, if places were not too far apart, he would sleep alternate nights in each, but managed the work in both. If we were lucky enough to book him for two or three days he would be off to his next appointment almost as soon as we returned. He charged nothing, and would accept nothing other than his food, but was insistent that we all remembered to leave him notepaper, envelopes and stamps (first class only) as Dudley was an avid letter writer. Lord Cottesloe always left him House of Lords headed notepaper, as did one or two others. He wrote to friends all over the UK and several abroad, mainly local youngsters who were sheep shearing or on some sort of agricultural course in Australia or New Zealand. Then there were foreign girl grooms, French or Dutch or Italian, who had met Dudley at some of the residences where he was house-sitting, and struck up a firm friendship with the loveable old rascal. He never had a bad word to say about anybody. 'If you can't say something good about your fellow critters,' he would assert, 'then don't say anything at all.'

Before he left for his next appointment he would sit the F/H/B on a kitchen chair, drape a towel round his neck with a grandiose flourish, produce scissors from his carrier bag, and give him a haircut. This was a ritual that was anticipated by all his clients, even looked forward to. 'If I don't do it you'll have to go to Exeter,' he would say. 'And who the hell wants to go there unless 'tis for a haircut or to get drunk.'

Being a good barber, he left a trail of satisfied customers and once finished he would return the scissors to the paper carrier that contained his shaving kit, red silk pyjamas, a small tub of Gentleman's Relish, which he never travelled without, and a bundle of corks which he stuffed into his bed at night as a remedy for cramp. On the back seat of his decrepit old Mini there rolled, untethered, a bottle of Grouse, and his dog, Pilgrim in the front passenger seat. He was a Dorgi, a cross between the Queen's Corgi and Princess Margaret's Dachshund and given to Dudley by one of his lady clients, who told him it came from Royalty. 'The Queen, I think,' he had told us. 'Not that I know the Queen personally, you understand.' It would not have surprised us if he had, he knew just about everybody, and corresponded regularly with Dick Hearne, whom he did know personally, and lunched with at Badminton annually on the Duke's Puppy Show day.

We would always wave Dudley off the premises when he left, then go back inside and worry for him. He was a menace on the road and could see no sense in paying out good money for petrol when driving downhill, which resulted in him switching off the engine on one-in-four gradients and free-wheeling from top to bottom. If there was a sharp turn at the end he usually attempted that, too, but he never had an accident, although he was probably the cause of hundreds. He did hit the water trough in our yard once, cracking the stonework. 'Damn silly place to stick a water trough,' he observed amiably to the F/H/B who had watched mesmerised as Dudley's old car silently swooshed down the hill, wildly swinging right-handed into the yard, narrowly missing two barns, but smashing into the water trough.

'That trough was there 'afore you wuz born,' the F/H/B told him, peevishly surveying the damage.

'Then 'tis high time you had a new one,' came the answer. 'And put'n back out the way a bit, not where I can smack into'n!'

Dudley's great friend over the years was a distinguished looking gentleman from Worcestershire called Bill Barker, who stayed with us for a fortnight every autumn, following the hunt by car. Dudley was always working at somebody's house but would commence at the crack of dawn so that he could present himself at Chilcott as soon as Bill had finished breakfast. I would hand them their Thermos and sandwiches for the day, and the two would set off; Bill in his tweeds and polished brogues, tall, upright, military, with a waxed moustache, and Dudley, who was dapper with a faded dandy look, wearing moleskin trousers with one leg cut shorter than the other (for some reason all his trousers were the same), shoes with odd laces, a red spotted handkerchief with a curly edge flopping from the breast pocket of his old tweed jacket, a large flower in his buttonhole, and the whole topped by the former racehorse trainer, Vincent O'Brien's rakish hat which Dudley had won from him in a wager at Cheltenham Races.

From time to time they travelled in Bill's splendid two-tone green Bentley but he found it difficult to manoeuvre in our narrow lanes and he was ever fearful of getting it scratched. Once, when it was slightly damaged by Dudley backing his Mini on to it in the yard, Bill Baker all but cried, though the resultant scratch was scarcely visible. Dudley dismissed it airily. 'Sorry, Bill, but nothing there that a lick of paint won't cover!' The scratch was eventually eliminated at the Rolls Royce Centre at Cheltenham, and Bill footed an account of £135 in lieu of Dudley's 'lick of paint'.

He recounted this to me on the telephone, adding crossly that it might teach Dudley to look where he was going if he sent him the bill. 'You do that,' I told him. 'But just remember to go to China for your next holiday.' 'You win,' he said, with the sigh of a man who has battled against overwhelming odds and lost.

'You can't put a price on friendship,' I told him.

It was out of the question for Bill to travel in his friend's Mini as his tall frame could never have folded sufficiently for him to fit in, and anyway, it was Pilgrim's prerogative to occupy the front seat. This impasse led to them borrowing our pig van for days at a time, and the two elderly gentlemen seemed to derive the most amazing pleasure from bounding, none too comfortably, through the narrow lanes unhampered with technicalities like a petrol gauge, handbrake or hooter. The first day he borrowed the van, Bill, concerned over the petrol gauge which permanently registered E, decided to refuel in Dulverton before Dudley arrived to accompany him on their day out. So fearful was he of being stranded that he gratefully accepted the offer of another guest to follow him in his own car to the garage. He parked on the slope outside the petrol pumps and got out to thank the other driver who had pulled in opposite, but as they talked they were horrified to see the driverless pig van slide slowly past them backwards down the hill. It came to no harm as the pavement jutted outwards and stopped it, but Bill, when he recounted it to us, sounded as though he died a thousand deaths in those few seconds.

'You shoulda put'n in bottom gear when you parked,' I said reprovingly.

'But, my dear, I put the handbrake on,' he protested.

'That one don't work,' I answered dismissively. 'Now don't you go forgetting, bottom gear every time you stop. And take a can of petrol. Oh, and the hooter's never worked, neither.'

Bill, as No. 1 Driver, mastered the hooterless pig van eventually and if anything got in the way solved the problem by simply sticking his head out of the window and bawling 'Perp-perp!' and if the obstruction did not shift, were it a sheep, pony, deer, or even a tractor, Dudley would encourage, 'Louder, Bill, louder, 'tis no good sounding like a tin whistle in a thunderstorm!'

Bill told us he found it difficult to keep a hold on the bumpy steering and avoid looking at the mesmeric petrol indicator on E, whilst his companion, in the passenger seat, with Pilgrim at his feet, kept up an intense running commentary on the countryside, the farmers, the livestock, the deadstock, and the wildlife. If he thought his friend's concentration was wavering he would say sharply, 'I'm telling you all this now, and in half an hour's time I shall be asking you questions on it, so just pay attention, Bill!'

Once, when Dudley himself was not paying attention, Pilgrim climbed from the front to the back and devoured their sandwiches. When lunchtime came and they reached for their carrier, all that remained of their favourite sausage sandwiches were a few crumbs on a bit of greaseproof paper.

'Your damn dog's eaten our sandwiches,' accused Bill.

Dudley showed immediate concern. 'God help us. Was there mustard on them?'

'How the hell should I know,' rounded Bill. 'I never even tasted them, did I?'

Dudley looked worriedly at Pilgrim, the picture of innocence. 'Only Pilgrim doesn't like mustard,' he said.

'You tell that to somebody else,' snarled the enraged Bill. 'I'm driving to the nearest pub for a slap-up lunch and Pilgrim can bloody well pay for it!'

Very often, after these expeditions, Dudley would drop off in the late afternoon at his place of residence, complete his tasks whilst Bill took a nap in a chair, then come on to Chilcott for dinner, eating in the dining room with his friend. As the same people were booked for that same fortnight every year, Dudley was well known to all of them, and was always treated as the guest of honour. The large party came from the Midlands, where they were all engaged in industry but one year they informed us that one of their colleagues, at that time unknown to us, had taken the cloth and been appointed Rector of Exford Parish. They intended to visit him during their stay, so we sent an invitation for him and his wife to dine with their old friends at Chilcott. He turned out to be a racy raconteur, and the invitation became an annual one, which resulted in us enjoying many a lively night with the parson and his wife, Bill Barker, Dudley, and the Birmingham crowd, who always arrived with a plentiful supply of very fine wine. Dudley, however, never drank when he was eating, having been told by a witch doctor some time in his colourful past, that it was bad for the system to mix food and drink at the same time. After the dinner we all anticipated his next move, which involved accepting a large Grouse and drinking to the 'Health of the Ladies, Lord bless 'em,' then presenting his glass for a second one, with the artless statement 'A bird can't fly on one wing!'

One of the highlights of Bill Barker's fortnight was when he and Dudley were invited by friends to join them at dinner at the Crown Hotel in Exford. The dinner was always referred to as the AGM, and Dudley, as the oldest member, acted as chairman. Dining in Exford suited him, as at that time he was close by, usually working just up the steep hill out of the village, at Stone, whilst the owners went deer-stalking in Scotland.

We always waited up for Bill to return home from Exford. Very often there would be a distinct autumnal chill in the air and he would be grateful for one of the F/H/B's hot toddies whilst he recounted details of the dinner and the 'minutes' of that particular year's AGM.

One year, though, it was a wonderful Indian summer evening, and our guest settled for a straightforward whisky, whilst reporting how, having arrived early at Exford, he and the half-dozen other friends attending the AGM decided to wait outside the hotel for Dudley. They stood in a group, chatting, with drinks in their hands, at the bottom of the steep hill, just at dusk, with the late roses scenting the evening air. Their tranquillity was shattered by the sighting of Dudley's old Mini, free-wheeling down the hill, as usual, at a crazy speed but with a spec-tacular blaze of sparks detonating from the off-side, as though it were about to burst into flames. The little group of friends watched in pet-rified silence as he overshot the hotel by some distance, then rolled slowly backwards to where they were standing, unaware of their concern. Their fears for Dudley's safety were soon allayed when they realised the sparks were not from a mechanical fault but from the metal catch on the seat belt, which, unbuckled as usual, Dudley had slammed in the door and was dragging along the road.

They were in for another surprise when he got out, because, for the first time ever, he was sporting a new hat for that very auspicious occasion. It was a too-large Stetson that someone had given to him and which he had attempted to cut down to suit his more diminutive size by chopping a couple of inches off round the brim with his hair-dressing scissors, leaving a ragged edge, as though a mouse had been chomping at it in the night.

Their AGM was away to a flying start that year but Dudley's new hat was such an object of fun that it made its first and last appear-ance, and was never seen again, not by anybody. Bill reckoned it ended up in the River Barle. Material possessions never meant any-thing to Dudley, anyway, people and horses and hounds and deer crowded everything else out of his life.

He was at Stone, which was probably his favourite place, when he felt slightly unwell. It was on a Friday, and the farm manager there sent for a doctor (Dudley would never have done such a thing), who suggested he went to hospital for observation. He was taken to Minehead and told his nurse, 'If I die, don't tell anybody, then they won't miss me.' He died two days later, just short of his ninety-third birthday. The Devon and Somerset Staghounds held a Memorial Meet for him at Molland Moor Gate and hundreds turned up, local and from all over the country, to pay their respects to a Grand Old Man, loved by all.

Chapter Eleven

The F/H/B has always maintained that a certain type of person, abruptly transported from town to country, suffers a strange metamorphosis, almost as though the sudden transition form urban to rural life is more than the body can take in one swift journey down the motorway. It manifests itself in different ways, some more interesting than others. Many find the country air soporific and after a day on the moors quietly snooze over their dinner, whilst others toss sleepless in their beds because it's too quiet, or too dark and they miss the street lights or even the traffic whooshing up and down outside their windows. Others react like Mrs Lock.

Mrs Lock arrived with her husband, a silent, surly man in his fifties, and a small pug dog that seemed to be permanently clamped to her large, capable bosom. Everything about her was capable, from her common-sense greying hair drawn into a tidy bun, to her home-knitted sweater and tweed skirt, and the sturdy legs ending in ribbed tights with ankle socks and stout walking shoes.

At bedtime, on the first night of their holiday, there was a gentle knock on the kitchen door and Mrs Lock thoughtfully came to bid us goodnight. 'It was a delightful dinner, my dear, and I did appreciate it,' she said graciously. Then a word for the F/H/B, engrossed in his Saturday Sunshine Puzzle at the kitchen table. 'I've been watching you from my bedroom window – such a busy life you lead!' Scarcely had the kitchen door closed behind her as we chorused our goodnights, than it was flung open again and she re-appeared with what I can only describe as a dramatic flourish. 'My name,' she told us, 'is Olga.'

From then on Olga established the kitchen as her base, appearing before breakfast and after breakfast, before dinner and after dinner, clasping her little pug dog and crooning to it to 'Come to Olgie-Wolgie.' I noticed when she said it her eyes were riveted on the F/H/B.

Of Mr Lock there was little sighting, other than at meal times. He was a silent, singularly uninspiring man spending long hours alone in the bedroom which led me at first to think he might be religious. But there were no Bibles, songsheets or sacred books to indicate that some form of religion obsessed him. It turned out he was a shop steward and worried about the election, which was the coming

Thursday, and he thought Labour was likely to lose again to the hated (he said) Margaret Thatcher. His wife appeared to ignore his preoccupation with politics, her attitude being you-do-your-thing-and-I'll-do-mine; her thing, she told us, being amateur dramatics, which explained the flourishes and dramatic entrances and exits, if only to the kitchen.

One night, early in the week, Olga arrived as usual, in the kitchen, and placing her capacious black bag carefully on the table, withdrew from it a bottle of whisky. 'Now,' she said, hauling herself out of her chunky cardigan, 'if you'll just tell me where the glasses are, we'll all have a cosy little drink together.'

If the lady's eyes were riveted on the F/H/B, then mine were riveted on her. The formidable cardigan had concealed a flowered, softly gathered skirt and an amazing off-the shoulder black velvet top that revealed Olgie-Wolgie was definitely all-woman. I noticed the ribbed tights and ankle socks had given way to something more sheer, and even the clumpy shoes had been replaced with lighter ones. The drinks were poured, and by the third or fourth whisky Olga and the F/H/B were joking together like old mates in a pub, with her leaning alarmingly towards him across the table, which brought to mind an old seaside postcard bearing the caption 'Madam, your dumplings are boiling over!' She finally swept out in one of her grand stage left exits, leaving behind mixed fumes of Youth Dew and Fine Old Grouse.

The following evening, before dinner, Olga was back in the kitchen to collect her dog's food, which I kept in the dairy. I went through to get it, leaving her chatting to the F/H/B and must have been quicker than usual, because on re-entering the kitchen I witnessed the amazing spectacle of Olgie-Wolgie steam-rollering determinedly towards my husband, who was backing away, with arms out-stretched to save himself, and stammering 'Now steady on, missus, steady on!'

Standing rooted in the doorway in my wipe-over pinny with a piece of tripe in my hand, I endeavoured to look detached and dig-nified.

Olga must have seen the change of expression in her landlord's face as he caught sight of me, for she quickly whirled around. 'My goodness,' she trilled, 'what splendid fun we're having. I'm teach-ing him to samba!' 'Here's your tripe,' I said coldly, as the dancers separated.

For the rest of the week the F/H/B kept a fairly low profile when Olga invaded the kitchen, although for all I knew they could have been samba-ing round the yard twice daily.

On Election Day Olga suggested they drove us in their car to the Parish Rooms to register our votes, which we always did together and with great ceremony. Mr Lock looked as though it were the last place he wanted to go, knowing by then that we were not on the same wavelength, but his wife insisted, 'Come along, Albert, then your girlfriend can sit in the front next to you.' What was she on about, I wondered, who was his girlfriend? I soon found out when she climbed into the back and beckoned the F/H/B in beside her whilst I was left to sit in front with the savage looking Albert who looked as though he would as soon have travelled alongside Margaret Thatcher.

I knew all about feelings running high at election time inasmuch as, before the F/H/B trained me to vote Conservative, I was a Liberal. We lived on the other side of the moor then, in the North Devon constituency, and in defiance of the F/H/B's wishes, I joined the village Liberal party, where I was catapulted into high office as treasurer, with fourteen fully paid-up members. Our funds were kept at home in a pudding basin on top of the shelf of the kitchen dresser until I discovered that the F/H/B, whilst loudly voicing his disapproval of my political affiliations, was not above dipping his hand in the pudding basin when he was short of a pound, which I was left to replace. In the lead-up to the General Election we attended meetings together of the three leading parties, both in the village and in Barnstaple, and there was a lot of good-natured banter between us, with me sticking my Jeremy Thorpe poster on the gatepost at dead of night, only to find it replaced by morning with a Conservative one.

On Election Day the rivalry had become more heated with (1) my announcement at breakfast that I would be taking my stand at the Polling Station for a two-hour stint on behalf of the Liberals, and (2) before I left, with the F/H/B nowhere to be seen, I was inspired to climb a ladder to the top of my cherished Buddleia tree and hook a Jeremy Thorpe poster on the highest branch. This was a particularly devious action on my part, aware that the F/H/B suffered from bad vertigo and was unlikely to consider it worth the strain of climbing a ladder just to remove a rival poster. That, I chuckled to myself, was one that would definitely not be replaced with a Conservative one. I was right. When I returned home my beloved Buddleia lay on its side in the garden, sawn down in its prime, with Jeremy Thorpe still attached, but face down in a lump of mud. Feelings were, indeed, running high.

Back to the present election, I had sympathy for Albert whose conscience as a shop steward must have rebelled at being bulldozed into driving known Conservatives to the polling station, but he was no match for his wife at her most strident.

We took them into the pub and bought them drinks but the place was filled with election fever and Albert must have felt he was in some alien land. It seemed a long three-mile drive home.

Albert refused to watch television that night, and stumped huffily off to his room. The Conservatives won their expected victory, and next morning at breakfast a pleasant little lady guest from Essex remarked that Neil Kinnock was probably not feeling too happy that day. The shop steward turned on her, all his pent up rage surfacing. 'Have you met him?' he snarled at her.

'Er, no, no, of course not,' she stammered.

'Well I have, and he's a damn nice chap, worth more than all you bloody Conservatives put together.' He stormed out, slamming the door.

'What's he on about?' asked the little Essex woman of her husband. 'We've always voted Labour.'

On the Saturday morning Olga and her husband left, as they had arrived, he, dour and unsmiling, and she clad in her sensible sweater, tweed skirt and ankle socks. We saw them off, then returned to the kitchen to find on the table a bottle of Chivas Regal with a card tied on with a red ribbon, and inscribed in large capitals to MR HUXTABLE. The message read 'O Handsome Prince, don't ever change.' Beside it was a paper bag, also inscribed in large capitals, to MRS HUXTABLE, but with no message. Inside was a tin of Boots lightly fragranced talcum powder. The F/H/B was not looking in my direction. I waited. He spoke very slowly. 'Interesting, very interesting,' was all he said.

'I'll bet it was,' I told him.

◇◆◇

Although some holidaymakers appear to transform on their journey from town to country, there are others whose partners would frankly welcome them to change but rarely succeed in so doing. Such were a couple of publicans and their wives from Hertfordshire who were given our address from their milkman, a cheery gentleman, who had spent many holidays with his family at Chilcott.

The four friends arrived together in a massive old grey Rover and the husbands good-humouredly introduced themselves. 'Our wives are Gladys and Mavis and we're Monkey and Shakey. No, I'm not joking, everybody calls us that, so you must as well.' They were jolly, likeable fellows and obviously looked on a farmhouse holiday as a bit of a lark. They told me all their previous holidays had been spent bed-and-breakfasting in pubs, hotels and various licensed premises, but this time they were indulging their wives – just for once, they emphasized – who craved a holiday away from the saloon bar. Obviously the wives cherished hopes that a 200-mile drive down the motorway to a remote farm would be the magic formula for a teeto-tal holiday. They were pleasantly plump, dignified ladies, probably approaching retirement, whilst both the husbands had a lean and hungry look, being tall, elongated men; Monkey balding with a sad looking droopy moustache and Shakey with sparse sandy coloured hair spread thinly across his head. Neither conformed to a pub-lover's image. The reason for their lean, almost gaunt appearance, manifested itself at the dinner table on the first night. They both tackled their celery soup dotted with swirls of fresh cream but the main course of roast lamb and mint sauce produced an instantaneous and devastating effect. With one accord they crashed back their chairs from the table and fled from the dining room. Seconds later Monkey returned and snatched up their two unused water glasses before rushing out again. The wives looked at one another signifi-cantly and tut-tutted. 'Don't worry, my dear,' Mavis told me. 'It's the way they are, they're not used to dinner, we've only ever taken bed and breakfast in the past, but we're enjoying it, aren't we, Gladys?' Gladys nodded her approval, 'You can say that again,' she enthused, reaching for more buttered swede.

After the dessert they thought their husbands might like coffee. 'But not in here, dear, don't be offended, but the smell of food just upsets them.'

I carried a tray of coffee through to the sitting room to find my missing diners happily lounging in armchairs, their water glasses half-filled with whisky. They looked settled and contented and Monkey confided, 'Don't mind us, gel, this,' indicating the whisky, 'is what keeps us ticking.' Shakey raised his glass high, gazing at the golden liquid therein and they both solemnly drank to this statement of fact.

The next day I discovered that serious drinking commenced first think in the morning when I took their tea round at 8am. On waking, both Monkey and Shakey reached under their beds for their whisky bottles, Shakey warning me on the first day as I poured the tea for him and Gladys, 'Stop at half a cup, gel, I'll see to the other half!'

Breakfast was a non-starter for the Publicans, being a repeat of the previous evening, with them entering the dining room but rushing out again when they sniffed the bacon and eggs. They both had delicate insides, they informed me, with food aggravating their innards; they just were not used to it. 'If you feel you must give us something,' said Monkey considerately, 'make it a prairie oyster, just whip up a nice raw egg in an optic of vinegar, and that'll do us for breakfast.'

I carried their prairie oysters and some coffee to the sitting-room where they had spread out a map of Exmoor and were planning their day. They sounded quite sensible and seemed anxious to indulge their wives in the sight-seeing that Gladys and Mavis referred to as 'a proper holiday'. Gladys in particular confided that she loved the sea, and as we are only just over 20 miles from the coast, she set Minehead as her target for a day's outing.

I soon realised, along with the wives, that every day carried the same hopes that never materialised. The old Rover stopped automatically at every pub, and by the time the lunchtime session was ended, Monkey and Shakey were ready to turn homewards for a quiet sleep. From then on, bottles of whisky would appear from the most unlikely places like rabbits from a magician's hat. Once Shakey dived into Monkey's pocket and whipped from it a bottle which he flourished on high with one hand, trumpeting through his other hand 'Ta-ra, ta-ra'. On another day they arrived back with new welly boots, which they used as containers, drawing from them yet more bottles. They were fired with enthusiasm to walk the farm, but somehow the boots remained in a neat line in the cider room, pristine and un-muddied although the contents disappeared. One bottle turned up in the F/H/B's milking bucket which was standing empty in the cowshed and he was suitably grateful, waving his check cap and yelling, 'That's the best bucket of milk I ever seen,' before carefully placing his treat behind a bale of hay.

I feared for the Publicans at night because they so obviously missed a saloon-bar atmosphere on the farm that they had taken to driving the three miles to the nearest inn. Although their wives went with them, neither had driven for years and their husbands were never in a fit condition to drive home. Shakey hit the hedge on the first night and Monkey hit the gatepost on the second. The third night Mavis managed to steer the battered Rover home without mishap, but forgot to put on the hand-brake in the yard and it rolled downhill into the water trough. It was late and they all went straight to bed whilst I finished ironing sheets in the kitchen and the F/H/B drained a night-cap before going to his roost. Everywhere was quiet until I became aware of footsteps walking around upstairs. Not the ordinary sound of someone walking to the bathroom but more of a non-stop pacing and the sound of doors opening and shutting on their old latches. Then the steps faded in the direction of the front stairs, so I thought it timely to investigate.

I found Monkey, dressed in stripy pyjamas and a sports coat, descending the stairs one at a time, then stopping and deliberating before taking the next step. At first I thought he was sleep-walking and I rushed to take his arm but Monkey was wide awake and very upset. 'It's Mavis,' he said, 'she's gone. I bin in all the rooms and looked in all the beds, but I can't find her. She was there when I went to the bathroom, now she's gorn.' His voice rose to a wail. ''Tis all right,' I soothed him. 'You come alonga me and we'll soon find your Mavis.' I led him back up the stairs to his room where Mavis lay fast asleep in the far side twin bed, helped him off with his sports jacket, wondering why he had put it on in the first place, and tucked him into his bed.

The next morning there were hoots of raucous laughter over Monkey's nocturnal inspection of ladies in adjoining rooms as they lay in their beds with their hair in curlers. Monkey entered into the spirit of it, saying he wished he had been sober enough to remember them all. One thing is certain – they never forgot him.

With two days left to go to the end of the week Monkey and Shakey decided to pull out from the rural life and book B&B in the local pub, not only to save their car from another battering but they seemed to think they had indulged their wives' whims for quite long enough. 'Mustn't let these womenfolk get away with too much or they'll take some handling,' Shakey winked to the F/H/B as they settled their bill for the full week. 'You can say that again Squire,' said the F/H/B. 'Only two things in these parts you got to beware of and that's intelligent women and intelligent pigs. Can't keep neither in their sty, always wants to see what's on the t'ther side.'

I felt sorry for the wives, although it was obvious their husbands never intended to relate to their dreams of a country holiday. Tramping round fields and woods, even in new wellies, and working up hearty appetites was not for them. And now Gladys' longing to see the sea seemed even more remote. I mentioned this to Shakey, and he was happy to set the record straight. 'Took her yesterday,' he told me then, turning to his wife, 'didn't I, my dear?' 'Well, sort of,' replied Gladys. I was puzzled. 'How do you mean, sort of? Either you did or you didn't.' Shakey tilted a little to the left, then straightened again. 'Well, in the first place,' he said matter-of-factly, 'it's a waste of good drinking time driving to a place like Minehead just to look at bloody salt water, so, I drove up a damned great hill, can't remember where, but Gladys could look right across to the Bristol Channel. It was raining a bit but you could see it all right, couldn't you, my dear?'

'Just. It was miles away,' grumbled Gladys. 'Ten at least,' I agreed, recognising their look-out. 'Now look, Gladys,' said Shakey patiently, 'you wanted to see the sea. Right. Now did you or did you not see it?'

'Well I was hoping we might have gone...' commenced the hapless wife.

'Yes or no,' interrupted her husband in a louder voice. 'Did you or did you not see it?'

'Yes,' said Gladys meekly. 'Well stop belly-aching and be grateful,' Shakey told her sternly, as they left to load their luggage and drive the three miles to their new accommodation in Dulverton. It probably felt like going home after five days in a penitentiary.

By an odd coincidence, another couple who had been staying for the same week had arranged their away-from-it-all holiday in order to distance the husband from the heavy drinking sessions involving his job. Teddy Walker was a Londoner who had spent the wartime years evacuated to my father-in-law's farm in North Devon and the F/H/B, his brother George and sister Stella had forged firm friendships with the little cockney lad. After the war he worked on the farm for a while but eventually returned to his parents' home in Wandsworth ('should never have left Devon, biggest mistake I ever made'). He later joined the Gordon Highlanders and became a bandsman, playing bagpipes, then he left, married a charming lady and joined a shipping firm. His easy-going manner enabled him to work his way up from office boy to trouble-shooter, liaising between his firm and the then strike-ridden dockers who were forever calling lightning strikes involving his firm's ships. Most of the liaising was conducted in quayside pubs involving drinking sessions that made Exmoor farmers on market day look as if they were on a self-denial pilgrimage. This, coupled with the stress of getting the ships out of dock, had brought on a near-fatal heart attack which forced him into early retirement and a re-think of his whole life style.

Teddy was a classic example of a man who had ruined his own health drinking the health of everybody else's, and, having to refuse Monkey and Shakey's generous offerings, had been a daily embarrassment. It made us all wonder how much longer the Publicans could keep up the punishing pace they had set themselves, for, besides the whisky, they smoked 50 cigarettes apiece every day. But no more than two matches!' boasted Monkey proudly. The farmhouse that week stank like a four-ale bar, said Teddy Walker loftily, and it was obvious there is nothing more repellent to a newly abstemious convert than to be reminded of his bad old ways. He was, nevertheless, concerned for the likeable old rogues, ruminating darkly, 'Their turn'll come, you mark my words.' The F/H/B was more happy-go-lucky. 'Nort that a good old dose of Tippers drench won't cure, I'll warrant,' he proclaimed. Tippers drench was an old West Country antidote for all ailments. A veterinary product, it was a fiery concoction prescribed originally as a cattle drench, it turned out to be kill or cure for not only most animals, but also found favour among the local human population, notwithstanding the label on the squat brown bottle directing that dosage should be according to the age, size and strength of the animal, guaranteeing the bonus of promoting a glossy coat and alert expression.

The local doctor is aware that he is consulted not only after Tippers drench, but after the wart charmers, bullrushes, magic words, cobwebs stuffed in open wounds and homemade potions have all failed. He has trained himself to diagnose from the smallest crumbs of information in the local farmspeak. 'What's wrong today then Farmer?'

'Reckon I got a touch of the nadgers, sir.'

'Oh, quite. Er, where do you feel this?'

'Well I ain't sure if 'tis the nadgers or the lurgy. One or t'other. 'Tis me guts, like.'

Taking the initiative is to the doctor's advantage, sizing folk up and talking in a language we all comprehend. 'Hetty, you're like a great fat sow. Tell me what you had for breakfast this morning.'

'Oh, lemme think a minute, Doctor. Now then, there was a rasher of fat bacon, one – no, I tells a lie – two lamb chops, egg, fried bread and a coupla pound of taters.'

'It's no wonder you look in-pig!'

'You won't put me on no diet, doctor, will 'ee?'

'I am not a witch doctor, Hetty, I cannot magic away fat. You'll go on a diet and three months from now I'll have you looking like a skin-tered cow.'

Country children are brought up tough, and there can be a notice-able contrast between them and visiting children from towns. One small boy was a self-imposed vegetarian at eight years old and sported smelling salts with, 'I think I've got a cold coming – oh dear, I shall be ill with worry.' Another small hypochondriac averted his head from his plate at breakfast, advising the assembly in general, 'You should never sniff an egg, it's very bad for you.'

One child I expected to have a tougher uphringing was born to a childless couple who came to stay at least once every year. They helped out with all the farm jobs, but it was after cleaning out the pig houses that the wife found herself pregnant with the longed-for baby. Eventually a card announcing the birth arrived, but it was not the conventional 'God's gift of a daughter'. It read 'Powerful stuff that old pig shit.'

Chapter Twelve

A lot of people talk about the town/countryside divide and, with the interests on both sides becoming increasingly diverse, the gap seems to widen annually. Nevertheless, locals who are in the B&B trade often form strong lifelong friendships with visiting townsfolk, who often claim Exmoor as their second home. When such solid relationships are forged, we each take on a little bit of the others' lives, though usually we have scant idea of where exactly they live or of their lifestyle once their holiday is finished and they leave for home. Waving our goodbyes as they set off up the hill in their cars would turn into an annual anticipated little pantomime with our visitors yelling through the car windows, 'See you next year' and the F/H/B bawling back, 'And if you can't come just send the money!'

Many visitors to Exmoor confide they are doing jobs they hate and are surrounded by people with whom, other than their work, they have little in common. They yearn, they tell us, for the clean, fresh air of the moors, the skylarks in the heather, and the clip-clop of horses' hooves. These are the tourists who often retire to Exmoor, and they are the ones who settle, usually, more easily than the people who are still in business. Even so, there are hurdles to be crossed. Often in their home towns, they say they scarcely know their next-door neighbours, which is a lifestyle – if that is the word – if pursued, so alien to the country that they might as well stay rooted in Tunbridge Wells, or wherever, rather than move to Exmoor where the Doing and the Giving is of paramount importance. They have to learn that in a village community Everybody supports Every doing. The Conservatives support the Liberals, the Liberals and Conservatives support the Women's Institute, the WI supports the Mothers and Toddlers, and they all support the British Legion and the Church Bell fund, not forgetting the Carnival. And by Doing and Giving, we participate. One retired businessman suggested that all the fund-raising events cease and everybody merely gave a fiver on each occasion and stayed home. He was regarded with pity, and this constituted his first Big Mistake. Incomers are permitted one Big Mistake, but if it is followed by a second then they might as well move to China. These are considered no-hopers, and there is no place for them on Exmoor. Some might have hit the big-time in the city but in the country it's not who you are but what you are that counts. Their money may buy a country mansion, but money does not buy a place in the hearts of the local community and the combination of money and no manners can kill the initial bonding stone-dead. They are known as the Bettermost folk and invariably consider themselves superior to those of us they have chosen to impress by their richness (they win on that), education (not always – they are often self-made and therefore tend to associate a peasant accent with a lack of schooling) and integrity (their dictionary sometimes differs from ours).

Bonding with the natives goes out with the slurry when a critical newcomer jumps right in it up to the top of their silver-buckled boots, momentarily forgetting they have left Kensington W1 and this is now their chosen land. One superior lady, newly settled in, did not endear herself to her neighbours when she called at the next-door farm and recounted to the farmer's wife details of a local radio interview she had heard that morning with what she described as a 'quite exceptional woman who had got up early every morning for the past two years to hand milk her Jersey cow.' The farmer's wife questioned the wonder of this, saying in effect, so what, plenty of farmers' wives milk a cow every day, but Superior Lady was not to be side-tracked, ramming home her punch line, 'But don't you see, this was not a farmer's wife. This was an educated person!'

We take it most people move here because they like it, so it is all the more astonishing when they want to change the place, particularly to do away with tourism. A lot who have been visitors themselves for a number of years assume a proprietorial attitude, with a down on caravans cluttering up the roads and even on the tourists themselves – 'They should never wear shorts and go without shirts in a place like Dulverton!' They may have a point here and there, but tourism is the lifeblood of a small Exmoor town. Some even refer to visitors despairingly as 'Grockles', a word the F/H/B would not tolerate being used in Chilcott, nor is it ever used by the locals. A retired businessman who used the word was told by the F/H/B to wash his mouth out, followed by, 'And the less I see of your sort, the better.'

The ones who settle here are rarely the people who report barking dogs, neighing horses or sheep with bad feet to the RSPCA/police/Department of the Environment (but never to the owners). Nor are they wise men from the east, who neglect to check the above-average rainfall in the South West, or the Hunt that regularly blocks the road outside their gateway. To them little things assume monumental proportions when it all starts to go wrong. One couple turned into a major calamity the absence of their favourite sweets and travelled 26 miles to Taunton to discover that Woolworth's Pick'n'Mix was inferior to Hounslow Woolworth's. They left. As the F/H/B said, it was a classic case of big trees from little acorns grow.

Another very determined lady announced in public that she and her husband had pledged to integrate by 'talking in funny voices and pretending to be country yokels.' If she was expecting a round of applause from us assembled yokels she must have been disappointed at the sudden stony silence that greeted her magnanimous gesture, which she then compounded by hastily adding, 'Not that country folk aren't very nice and awfully hard working!' Theirs was a short-lived stay.

The thought of retiring to the country seems to spawn idyllic dreams, a place where the sky is blue and the sun always shines, the husband tills the garden whilst the wife bakes bread and years of in-fighting are abolished, at a stroke. A bit like going to Heaven. The new peace usually lasts about a fortnight before the smoke signals start to go up, signifying the battle has merely moved from the east to the west. One retired wife, who had evidently spent her entire married life criticising her husband, was mortified to find that he was fast becoming a popular figure in the local community. She airily dismissed this with what she considered to be the reason, 'Yes, Patrick always manages to be popular with inferiors but antagonises his superiors, which is why he and I never got on.' The F/H/B, who happened to be one of the 'inferiors' that Patrick was popular with, leapt to his defence, rounding on the disloyal wife with, 'Call yourself well bred? I don't call *you* well bred,' to which she replied cuttingly, 'Well, I certainly don't call *you* well bred, either,' with the F/H/B coming back with, 'Ah! But I don't pretend to be!'

To cross the divide between the town and country cuts both ways, and it is quite likely that the majority of urban dwellers retiring to the country consider us natives an irritating lot. A couple who moved from Greater London to a cottage near us were strolling past our farm one afternoon when they were spotted by the F/H/B who invited them in for a cup of tea with the forthright, 'Come on in m'dears and tell us your business – 'twill save us a lot of time finding out!' After smiling at his audacity they realised he was in earnest, and fell in with the spirit of a new adventure. Countryfolk are interested, inquisitive and just plain curious and, as one ninety-year-old used to say when pumping newcomers for information, 'It 'in that *I* want to know, m'dears, 'tis if anybody asks!' which bears out the F/H/B's theory that bull baffles brain every time. Sound is said to travel faster than light on Exmoor, gathering momentum as it drifts across the moors, scandal becoming somewhat distorted in its progress, carried, so some insist, not by humans, or even the wind, but anonymously 'on they old lettuce leaves'. Tales abound, ranging from sightings of Seemingly's amorous sheepdog going about his depredations, to what goes on behind the pickle counter in the local store. This interest in our fellow beings highlights a serious misjudgement for folk on the wrong side of the law who consider a rural retreat necessary for a hidey-hole. Those attempting to conceal matters criminal may as well shout their sins from a soap-box on Hyde Park Corner as bring them to Exmoor; far fewer folk would take heed. Suspect behaviour is latched on to with, invariably, a demand for solitude, no forthcoming information, and, in the biggest cover-ups, a turn of aggression.

One lady who had all too obviously not moved to the countryside to drink in its natural beauty, unknowingly sawed through her own water pipe, but ferociously turned on her widowed neighbour, accusing her of persecution by deliberately sabotaging their shared water. She threatened, 'When I'm persecuted I get paranoid, and when I'm paranoid I get vindictive, and when I'm vindictive, everybody suffers!' The little widow was speechless at such savagery and made sure she locked her bedroom door every night. The aggressive neighbour sent for a repair man from Taunton, stating, 'I don't have nuffink to do wiv the locals.' She was obviously not on a budget, but the chickens came home to roost when her wood burner caught fire and the local brigade was called, Taunton being 26 miles away. She left.

It is scarcely surprising that curiosity runs rampant amongst the local population when strangers behave so at odds with a country lifestyle, where we all work together. A foreign lady who was renovating an old farmhouse even shipped goods and workmen from Sweden. Her stay was also short-lived but the purchaser of her property eventually discovered that there were no English replacements for the plumbing and central heating, which proved a costly venture.

Howsoever, all these folk ensure a fairish turnover for the estate agents. They call it re-distribution of wealth.

Seeking a little love-nest in the country away from prying eyes has to be one of the great myths of the countryside. Secluded it may be, but nowhere is ever too remote to escape the locals' keen observation of human behaviour, linked, it must be admitted, to an inquiring mind, particularly if the set-up is between what could be considered an ill-matched pair, leaving everybody receptive to gossip. A whispered 'That chap pays in £50 notes' hints at crime, whilst 'Her writes out the cheques' indicates either a bankrupt or a kept man.

Sometimes a little of their history precedes them, as it did the brisk, handsome tweed-suited lady in her mid-fifties, married, we were told, to a waxed-moustachioed retired colonel in Worcester who spoke at regimental dinners and lived for military matters. Nobody ever saw the Colonel in these parts but his wife, so rumour had it, had recently inherited a substantial legacy which she invested in an Exmoor cottage, into which she installed her constant companion, a good looking young stud in his twenties who addressed her as Auntie Darling. A famous London designer was retained to dismember the cottage and recreate it to the young man's instructions in French Provençal style. Auntie's nephew was reported to indulge his expensive taste, evidenced by ribbons of fancy wallpaper blowing across the neighbouring fields and fluttering in bramble hedges for years to come as timely reminders of how the young man lived alone in the dream cottage, with Auntie Darling arriving now and again around midnight then staying on for a couple of days. 'Like,' as the F/H/B put it, none too delicately, 'a large white arriving for service.'

It seemed to me the F/H/B and his cronies were more than a touch envious of a chap who spent his days sunbathing in the garden with a glass in his hand and a bottle of French red wine beside him, whilst the surrounding grass grew even higher. The farmers sweated over their sheep-shearing, carted their hay and worried over their corn and all but forgot about the young man ever-slumbering in the long grass. Their interest was re-awakened when they noticed he had been joined by a dazzling, ruby-lipped young French teacher on an exchange visit with whom he shared Auntie's best wine and she in return gave him French lessons. They went indoors for the lessons and the neighbours at the farm opposite thought they probably took place upstairs where the French mistress frequently appeared naked at a bedroom window. The inevitable happened when Auntie arrived unexpectedly one afternoon and disturbed her nephew in the middle of one of his lessons. As a colonel's lady she aired her knowledge of barrack-room expletives, followed by a fight resulting in a pile of broken glass, reputedly from the mirrored ceiling in the bedroom, and then Auntie, who was nothing if not a tough cookie, physically threw out the sinful pair. This was all graphically reported by the two delightful elderly sisters peeking over the dung heap from the farm opposite. The sad sequel was the French girl went home to France, pregnant and disgraced, and Auntie's nephew ended up in a pub washing glasses.

Auntie sold the cottage, minus the mirrors, at a loss and went home to the Colonel and his regiment. No one heard of them ever again. The two elderly sisters opposite were convinced the demon drink had a lot to answer for as there were 19 empty bottles in Auntie's rubbish bin. French ones!

Most people who uproot and retire to the country neither crave nor anticipate a wildly exciting life. Their dream is to swap No. 368 Cemetery Road for a cottage with a couple of acres with a Jersey cow, ducks and chickens, even a pig. They soon realise that animals demand a routine every day of the week, including Saturdays and Sundays, Christmas Day, birthdays, hung-over days. They can be forgiven a momentary sneaking nostalgia for the old life; reading the morning papers on the train to the office, finishing there at five o'clock, and a lie-in on a Sunday, instead of dreading milking the cow who's fidgety with sore titties and delivering stinging swipes with her tail, aimed to connect where it hurts most. Outside the cow shed predators are queuing up for the ducks and chickens, magpies and crows keep round-the-clock watch for new hatchings and there's work to be done on sheds and runs to make them fox-proof and rat-proof. The pig becomes one of the family and they can never eat it because they share a rapport which transcends black pudding and pork scratchings.

Then there's the dialect. As a tourist on a week's holiday it never seems to pose problems, but takes some overcoming when actually living with the locals. A favourite word is *drekly*, used mainly by plumbers/builders/electricians in the context 'I'll be up to see to your little job *drekly*' which can either mean next Christmas or next Easter, whichever comes last. *Rin*, meaning run, is used in North Devon but just over the border in West Somerset this translates as *urn*. This is a key word if Farmer Fred's bull is charging down the road, and must be memorised in both Devon and Somerset dialect. And remember you *apse* the gate, never shut it. Or use one word when half a dozen can be crammed in – unless you come up against an Exmoor windsucker who never utters yeay or nay but holds a conversation with mere sharp intakes of breath. There's nothing wrong with his vocal cords or vocabulary, this is just his chosen way to converse together with nods and shakes of his head.

With all of this to contend with it is not surprising that not all incomers get to grips with Exmoor. Paradoxically, the ones who are slightly uncertain about country living are more likely to be the long-stay ones, whilst the ones who proclaim that they have found Shangri-la and intend to stay until they go to the 'great farm in the sky' usually deport themselves within months, some avowing they loved the place but hated the people. This is not altogether surprising, what with the inquisitiveness, the plain speaking and being cut down to size, which has probably never happened in their lives before. One village where the locals were concerned with being taken over by townsfolk, elected one of the elders to visit any newcomers. He told them he welcomed them on behalf of the villagers, adding, 'And when you've lived here for ten years us'll ask your opinion on the way we run the place, but 'til then you keep quiet!' Some return to where they came from, but even then have been known, amazingly, to return to the moor for good.

The ones who stay, settle in comfortably and become popular dwellers in the villages. They often have time to devote to community work, toiling at meals on wheels, hospital car driving and arranging outings for the elderly. One lady was even unanimously elected Chairman of the Council. Like the F/H/B always says, think positive, and if there's ort you don't understand, then just keep nodding your head!

Chapter Thirteen

Being on such friendly terms with a number of our guests meant that we were very nearly 'family' and privileged to share their joys and sorrows. Two of these were Cecil and his wife Enid, a couple in their early fifties. Cecil was a big good-hearted Londoner and Enid was a petite little blonde, much more countrified, her parents having kept a corner shop and post office in Surrey. Cecil and Enid had two children in their twenties, but their lives revolved around one another.

Sadly, Enid fell ill and died at fifty-two, and Cecil was shattered to find himself having to rebuild his life. He rushed down to stay with us the day after the funeral, and paid several more visits in quick succession. The F/H/B instructed that I should go out with Cecil in his car most days and have a pub lunch, just to keep him company, as he was obviously devastated at losing his lovely wife and needed someone to talk to. He was inconsolable, and I was concerned that he was just fading away. Pub lunches and playing crib with the F/H/B every night combined with a copious intake of whisky, brought little respite to Cecil's sadness.

On his fourth visit, less than six months after Enid's death, a mystery lady telephoned every night of his holiday and had a lengthy chat with him. 'Just a neighbour worried about me,' he explained sensing our curiosity. I was disbelieving. I could tell from the eagerness in the woman's voice and a bit more spring in Cecil's step, that this was a liaison of some importance.

'Just you keep quiet, Maid, and all will be revealed,' instructed the F/H/B, as I answered yet another phone call from this new lady in Cecil's life. She was inclined to chat, garrulous even, revealing she was a part-time petrol pump attendant which was where she picked up with Cecil. 'Always dressed nice, always on his own and ever so lovely. So I thought "have a go, gel", says he'll bring me down to your place, but he'll have to pay 'cos I ain't got no bleeding money.'

The following spring, just about twelve months after Enid's death, Cecil phoned to book two single rooms for the following week. 'Cecil,' I said, 'just what are you up to, you know you can tell me?' 'Nothing,' he said emphatically, 'and don't you work anything into it. Everything's decent and above board.' Which is usually a statement meaning just the opposite.

A few days later the new lady telephoned to confirm the booking. 'Cecil says you got us down for two singles – dunno' what he's on about, we been living together every bleedin' weekend all winter.' She obviously wished to make their relationship quite clear and I sighed for the loneliness and vulnerability of the bereaved.

They arrived on a wet, windy afternoon and I noted the new lady was probably about the same age as Enid, but there the resemblance commenced and finished. Enid always wore subdued little print dresses that she sewed herself, but her successor was eye-catchingly clad in skin-tight ocelot leggings, high-heeled red patent boots and a short, swinging fake fur jacket. She was carrying a shiny yellow plastic holdall with a picture of Mick Jagger riveted on one side and pink plastic tulips on the other. She was all of 14 stone.

Cecil ushered her through the kitchen door and introduced her. 'This is Margie.' I heard the F/H/B catch his breath as he turned all his thoughts into one word 'un-bloodybelievable!'

Cecil's expression was that of a man who is suddenly aware that he has burnt his boats and there's no going back. They sat down and drank the tea I made, but the scones and cream were rejected by Margie, 'Nah, I'm on a diet, me, got to get a bitta this off,' and she slapped a plump ocelot-covered thigh. She was black haired with piercing heavily made-up eyes, encrusted in thick powdery blue eyeshadow. She jingle-jangled jewellery and I tried hard not to remember Enid with her dainty, understated little necklaces.

I showed them to their two rooms and as I went back downstairs I could hear Margie loudly protesting, 'What's all this about then, darlin', why we got to go through all this bleedin' pantomime just for them, that's what I wanna know.'

Dinner time was less than successful being doubly embarrassing for Cecil as, quite by chance, he and the other guests had met on previous visits. Margie inspected her roast lamb suspiciously and delivered a monologue to all in general, 'If my boy was here now, know what he'd do? He'd pick up his plate and chuck it against the wall. If it ain't pizza he don't wanna know. He don't put up with nuffink he don't like, he don't. Hit his headmaster last week over the head wiv a hockey stick. He don't put up wiv nuffink, not my boy.' Cecil kept his head down and said nothing.

The dessert was old-fashioned trifle made with cream, which Cecil rejected, saying he would go straight into the cheese and biscuits.

Margie, too, waved away the dessert with a be-ringed hand and a jangle of charm bracelets, and the words, 'If it ain't good enough for him then it ain't good enough for me! I'm subservient me, that's what I am, ain't I Cec?'

Cecil, who since his wife died, had spent his evenings after dinner in the kitchen with us, mercifully kept out that night.

The next morning, as soon as we were washed and dressed, the F/H/B and I walked into the kitchen together. There was loud music booming from the T.V. and somebody jumped on me from behind with a 'Boo! Guess who!' It was Margie, wearing a shortie dressing gown bunched round her middle, and hair in curlers. She was drinking tea from an ornamental mug I sometimes used for flowers. Somehow the whole kitchen looked in a state of chaos. The F/H/B strode over and switched off the blaring T.V. 'Do you always carry on like this in the morning?' he enquired coldly.

'Yeah, course I do 'ceps when I'm wiv Cec.' She closed one eye knowingly. I fancied that the F/H/B looked slightly non-plussed.

He addressed Margie brusquely. 'Look here,' he said, 'you can either sit down and keep quiet or you can get off upstairs, and next time you come down try and look a bit tidy – I don't expect my missus to slop around half-dressed, and I don't expect nobody else to, either.' He sounded magnificently severe.

'Coo, hark at him,' clucked Margie, then turning to me, 'I wouldn't put up wiv that if I was you.'

'Last night you was s'posed to be subservient,' retorted the F/H/B.

'Well only when I wanna be,' huffed Margie, slopping more tea into the flower mug and shuffling out through the door.

Breakfast time set the pattern for the rest of the week, with Cecil's lady friend establishing the tone of the conversation. She was, she expounded to her captive audience, an authority on miscarriages and knew a woman who bottled hers and kept it on her mantlepiece. She knew all about animals and did I know my ginger cat was about to have kittens. No, because it was a tomcat. Margie was in full spate and not to be side-tracked. 'Well, I can tell you any day now you're in for a big surprise.'

'But he's a doctored tom,' I protested in vain.

'Nah, nah, you're wrong there, somebody's having you on, you wanna get a proper vet. Used to have a cat, we did, when I was a kid, then me mum kicked the old man out and he took the bleedin' cat wiv him.'

I glanced at Cecil and saw him close his eyes, as though trying to shut out that voice. It was as though he had never heard Margie in full spate before. I mentioned it later to the F/H/B. 'I don't s'pose 'ee 'ave,' he said thoughtfully. 'Seems like they only meets weekends at his place and I shouldn't think they spends a lot of time talking politics.'

It was raining on the Monday morning and when eventually everybody left the breakfast table to go their separate ways Margie told Cecil she would be staying indoors for the day. 'You go out, mate, enjoy yerself. I ain't got no mac so I ain't going out,' she told him.

'Come on, gel,' Cecil said encouragingly. 'You won't get wet in the car. I'll drive you to Exeter.'

'What you fink I am? I'm telling you I ain't going no place wivout a mac.' I watched, mesmerised, as she went to work on our old friend, stroking his arm rhythmically with her fingers. 'Aw, you know me, Cec, I'd do anyfink for you, but I ain't going no place this bleedin' weather wivout a mac.'

'Well, why didn't you bring one, then?' asked Cecil politely.

''Cos I ain't got one, silly. Well, not a proper one. I only got half a job on them petrol pumps and the rest is on the Social, and I gotta watch me money, ain't I? I wouldn't be here if you wasn't paying for me, now would I? Oh, you're ever so good to me, Cec' – (she laid her face on his hand) – 'I'd do anyfink for you, honest, but I ain't going out wivout a mac.'

It was a cliff-hanger. I could have bet money that Cecil, who was nobody's fool, would see through Margie's game but to my amazement heard him say, 'Well come on then, let's go to Exeter and I'll buy you a mac. You can pick anyone you want.' The couple returned from Exeter after the shops shut, with Margie triumphant in a bright red waterproof with a detachable hood, plus two dresses, one yellow, one pink 'for when Cec takes me to his firm's do's 'cos I ain't got nuffink to wear.'

At dinner that night, Margie confided to the assembled guests that what she would really, really like would be a dear little baby, just like Cec. The guests were unsure whether to laugh or cry and one said, 'But haven't you already got a son?' 'Yeah, but my boy's fifteen now and his dad done a runner and left us both up the Khyber. Test pilot, he was, going to stand for Parliament next election.'

By Friday Margie decided things needed livening up a bit. She made a dramatic entrance at breakfast time screaming, 'Me handbag's gorn, lock all the doors, call the coppers, there was 200 quid in that bag.' The F/H/B told her in no uncertain terms to belt up, whilst Cecil started a systematic search, starting downstairs, and then moving upstairs to his bedroom where he found the missing bag behind the dressing table. 'Whaddya stick it there for, Cec? You going off yer trolley or somefink?'

That night the F/H/B managed to smuggle Cecil into the kitchen alone. He had to speak quickly before they were interrupted, telling him we were his old friends of many years standing, he was always welcome, and always would be, but don't ever, ever bring that woman again. Get rid of her, he said, and do it quick.

'I can't,' demurred Cecil. 'You've seen what she's like – she'll stand outside and throw bricks through all my windows, I know she will.'

'Let her do it, Cecil,' said the F/H/B. 'It'll be worth it in the long run – it'll pay off just to be shot of that baggage.'

Sadly, Cecil did not carry through the plan and he fell ill, probably through worry, and died in just a few months. A great gentleman we were proud to know.

Chapter Fourteen

I can never understand any woman who has ever been a landlady desiring children of her own. Association with other people's children in your own home, and outside on the farm, has got to be the biggest turn off ever. I have seen parents brought to their knees by stroppy kids, marriages split up, daddies relegated to the child's room whilst the Little Miracle moves into the double bed with mummy. A mother once told me, 'Your sheepdog is better behaved than my little boy' and I wholeheartedly agreed with her. Very often their own dogs are better behaved than the children and I knew which I preferred. It was no wonder I got what I called a 'touch of the Augs' in August, that being the main month for school holidays. I remember complaining once to the F/H/B that if I hadn't minded being pestered by children I might have desired some of my own, but I still had to put up with other people's. He replied that I should just grit my teeth and remember I was being paid to be pestered. His theory was that the blame for poor stock is usually with the sire and it only takes a long cool look at the stag that begat them for all to be revealed. Nevertheless, I felt that doting mummies played a part in their unlikeable offspring. One mummy indulged her child to the extent of eating 22 prunes at breakfast but the other guests were jubilant because they reckoned he wouldn't be appearing for the next two days.

Another mummy allowed her seven-year-old to go upstairs in the middle of dinner to collect a Mars bar to eat at the table. His dinner was pushed to one side and as he sat there munching his eyes fixed me in triumph with a you-dare-not-touch-me smirk. At times like that I felt almost saintly for resisting turning his dinner plate over his head. He finished the Mars bar and turned to his mother, speaking, it must be said, for all of us. 'Silly old twit,' he said, aiming a savage kick at her shins under the table.

It was a pity she couldn't have stayed the following week to absorb a few hints on child rearing from Siddy's mum, who at eighty-four still believed in good old fashioned discipline. Siddy was a very likeable bachelor of fifty-four, not at all wimpish, but aware that he had to toe the line with mother. He was reaching for his third slice of toast at breakfast when mother leaned across the table and rapped him sharply on the wrist. 'You've had enough, Siddy boy,' was all she said, but the toast dropped from Siddy's nerveless fingers. Maybe Siddy was one of those few children who start work early. This is always a pointer on farms. If a child is not working at four years old then it will never be any good, and this has been proven time and time again. There are obviously more jobs on farms for children than in towns, and they usually commence by feeding the chickens with corn and picking up eggs, then there are lambs to bottle and walking round the sheep with father. Howsoever, the more kids that join in the less work they do, which gives truth to the old adage, 'One boy's a boy, two boys is half a boy, and three boys is no boy at all.'

One family who stayed with us often and loved country life came from Middlesex. They were quiet, mannerly children and mother reckoned staying with us caused quite an upset in all their lives. Wendy, the eldest girl, wanted to be a teacher, but the F/H/B taught her to play cards, so instead of studying, every night after dinner she was shuffling and dealing with such expertise she could have gone professional. The son took to farming and stayed home to work every day whilst the youngest girl decided on a career with horses after the F/H/B started her riding. When she hit the ground now and then, her ruthless instructor would stand over her yelling, 'Get up, get back on that pony, NOW!'

The son's interest in farming led him to work for an animal feed company. The eldest girl abandoned her cards for long enough to pass her exams, and the youngest became a first-class rider.

It must be said that most children who visited the farm loved the animals, but they were instructed never to take animals in the house, their place being outside in the yard. This most certainly meant the hound puppies that we walked every year for the Dulverton East Foxhounds.

These were small and adorable when they arrived at eight weeks old, but rapidly grew into hefty long-legged rascals who knocked small children over and then licked their faces as they lay on the ground. Some kids were frightened, others enjoyed it. One puppy was called Fairy, a name the F/H/B flatly refused to use, an adorable little hound that was the only one ever to win me acclaim at the annual puppy show, 'First prize bitch, Mrs Huxtable'.

One rainy day I was worried when Fairy disappeared for an hour or so, but then a sweetly pretty, very mimpsey little girl who was staying with us whispered, 'Fairy's in my bedroom.' She had encouraged the young dog upstairs and then shut the bedroom door on her.

I think I screamed, 'No!' before taking the stairs two at a time, and as I opened the bedroom door I was hit by an unspeakable stench. Fairy was stretched out on the bed with her head on the pillow, like a little person. But Fairy had been rolling in the muck heap and was covered in cow dung, which partly accounted for the overpowering smell, the rest coming from flatulence motivated by the hefty dose of sulphur she had downed the night before. The bed and the room had to be taken apart and all but fumigated.

On holiday at the same time as the mimpsey little girl was another family with a small boy who was a little tough guy. The two children had nothing at all in common and the little girls parents obviously endeavoured to keep her well away from the boy who used embarrassingly colourful language for one so young. I wondered where he acquired his vocabulary as his parents were quiet and charming and obviously very worried about what he would say next. He had a throaty rasping voice and everybody in the house must have heard his loud rejoinder when he met the mimpsey little girl on the stairs as she picked up a flower and, waving it over her head, trilled in her little high-pitched voice, 'Here's a thing and a very pretty thing, what shall I do with this very pretty thing?'

The rasping answer came without hesitation, 'Stick it up yer arse!' The F/H/B decided that the lad definitely had potential and they became buddies with the boy learning to milk the cow and generally helping around the yard. In spite of his language, there was something likeable about him which is more than could be said of most of them.

In the summer we would let all six bedrooms and sleep downstairs in the old cheese room, opposite the sitting room and at the bottom of the front staircase (we had two – a lot of old farmhouses have a useful extra in the form of a back stairs). Our room was quiet, being away from the others, but on one particular Saturday morning one couple had opted to leave early and then insisted I did not get up as they would get their own tea and toast and be on their way before 6am. They were a great couple but the whole week had been spoilt by their aggressive three-year-old boy. I awoke about 5.30am to hear a petulant child's voice outside our door.

Little Benjamin had obviously been dumped at the bottom of the stairs whilst they loaded their car. 'I lost the pencil,' he was screaming. 'Somebody come and pick up me pencil.' He repeated it even more loudly and I lay rigid and quiet for fear the F/H/B would wake and not be too happy with the situation. The F/H/B was awake. He spoke. 'If I go out there and pick up that pencil his voice'll change.' I didn't doubt he meant it, but mercifully Benjamin was rescued in the nick of time.

I must admit being a landlady has coloured my attitude to children and I do not find it at all surprising that the more disciplined the child, the worthier adult they become. I may not love children in general, and even display above-average intolerance in particular at the first sign of a tantrum, but neither can I go along with Mummy (it's always Mummy, never Daddy) with the excuse that their dream child may not be perfect, but who wants a perfect child? Quite a lot, I should think, judging from the response at a Pony Club lunch where I was invited to give a talk.

It was held in a marquee at Cheddar and the M.C. was a brilliant local character whom I have known for many years. He gave me a great build-up, finishing with a grand flourish, and the words, 'And now, ladies and gentlemen, I give you – Norma Huxtable. Oh and by the way, she hates kids!'

The response was a cultured voice from the back of the marquee calling, 'Hear, hear! Don't we all?'

I thought a friend summed it all up very neatly at Dunster Show. A gang of noisy, uninterested children were elbowing us aside as we watched the grand parade of mares and foals, and the friend, exasperated, remarked, 'How can the young of the animal world be so endearing and Homo Sapiens not?'

Chapter Fifteen

In the 1970s and early '80s, farms, corner shops and village pubs were popular buys for townsfolk who opted out of what they called the 'rat race'. The shops and pubs proved too much work for too little return, but the lure of the farms gathered momentum, and by the late 1980s it became quite fashionable for suburban ladies to uproot husbands and families and move to the country. Real country, that is, like Exmoor and Dartmoor, where they would take over old farmhouses with a few acres and develop into 'dear little B&Bs'. It was trendy, allied to 'money for old rope' as one would-be landlady described it, and, above all, fun. To start with, though, perhaps the word 'landlady' was not quite the description they sought, so they became 'accommodation providers'. One such lady, on opening the door to her new guests put them right as to her social status with her first words to them, 'This isn't my job at all, I'm really a secretary!' Nor do they have empty rooms, like British Airways, they have instead 'availability'.

The trend is to be up-market with glossy brochures replacing our laboriously hand-written letters on sixpenny Woolworth's notepads. A number of these new ladies had not worked for the past twenty years or so, sailing through their suburban lives with the aid of a mother's help, a daily help and a gardener, before opting to roll up their sleeves and become landladies, chambermaids, cooks, confidantes and milkmaids.

A number of their husbands rightly followed their own career, but others, usually disastrously, attempted farming. Money would be spent on smartening up buildings besides renovating the old farmhouse and, finally, any left-over money went on livestock, which sometimes was not very much. An unforgettable advertisement in the local paper once read, 'Wanted. Cows and calves in exchange for new Land Rover and tractor'. One very new farmer managed to scrape together enough to buy a few pens of sheep, but not a ram. 'Going to do it yerself, then?' the F/H/B inquired innocently. The more prudent might merely exchange their suburban Range Rover with its tin of spray-on mud for a small economic car and a tractor with terminal rust spattered with genuine sheep's droppings.

Meanwhile the new landlady would, as like as not, decide on a school for their children 30 miles away. But there's no transport, so

Mummy has to make the journey twice daily, but no problem, she can fit it in after she's milked the new cow and before she prepares breakfast for the new guests. A minor hiccup arises when the new landlady finds it's not just B&B, it's evening dinner as well; they all want to eat in after a day out in the country but that should be simple enough. And in between breakfast and dinner she can make the beds, clean the house, do the shopping, milk the cow again, and collect the kids from their school 30 miles away. But think of the money – surely that makes it all worthwhile? Not so. It may be great for us hillbillies but these incomers are from cities and have hit the big time. They are appalled to find us all on what they consider to be impossibly low profit margins, and all costed out within a pound or two of the nearest neighbours, give or take an en-suite here and there.

One new arrival went into shock on seeing a local B&B and ED board advertising at £15 per night. She announced she would be starting at £20, and it only needed one to lead and all the rest would follow. The next day the £15 on the offending board was blacked out and £12.50 superimposed over it. She got the message. Nobody likes to see people arrive in Rolls Royces and go away on bicycles but happily this does not often happen. They leave because Exmoor is – Exmoor. One lady from Wandsworth who only stayed a few months encapsulated the whole place in a single sentence, 'I 'ate going uphill and I 'ate going downhill, I 'ate the wind and I 'ate the rain.' Many have never lived in the country before, their children have never experienced sleeping without a lamp-post outside their window, they miss the continual whoosh of traffic and police sirens and, worst of all, they are sharing their home with strangers. Mummy says she's doing it all for them, but the scenery and hedgerows don't mean a thing; they can't tell violets from periwinkles and don't care anyway. They are bought little furry animals to look after which, after a week or so, end up sad and neglected and would die of starvation if Mummy didn't add them to her list of growing dependants. Expensive ponies stand forlorn and muddy and neglected in the fields, whilst their young owners sit glued to the telly, growling bad-temperedly, 'I wanna go to Disneyland.' Getting the kids interested in gymkhanas could be a saviour in the dreaded school holidays and might even show results like a collection of colourful rosettes pinned to a plaque on the kitchen wall. One or two silver cups on the dresser, maybe...

One disappointed mum, watching her small child eliminated in the potato race on her 'guaranteed to win' pony, all but dragged her off as she exited the ring, screaming her frustration at the tearful child, 'You don't think we do this for fun, do you?' And then turning and yelling at the other mums, 'And there's me on Valium before all this!' If the mums were local, it was likely that few of them had heard of Valium. To our knowledge, none of us had before the influx of folk from the towns. It was then that Valium entered our vocabulary, together with Librium and panic attacks. Our own remedies cover most ailments, the majority having been handed down over the years. Like a spoonful of black treacle if anybody's a bit off colour, and that works wonders for sheep as well, whilst a sherry glass full of cod liver oil keeps the joints from seizing up.

And when it comes to oiling no self-respecting Exmoor man would travel in his truck without a bottle of Grouse under the seat, together with half-a-dozen plastic beakers (in case he meets up with his friends needing a quick pick-me-up). Our new men on the moor once settled, tend to introduce themselves to the nearest hostelry. This in itself can be quite revealing. One newcomer ordered a pint of lager, only to have the landlord look him straight in the eye and say slowly, and almost menacingly, 'I don't care a lot about serving that old foreign stuff. There's a decent cider in these parts.' The new boy, feeling somewhat deflated, was quick to agree. 'Oh, oh, yes, land-lord, most certainly. Make it cider, by all means,' and, as the landlord reached for a glass, 'er, could you put ice in it, please.' There followed a tremendous crash as a fist was thumped on the bar. 'Ice? You want ice in cider? What part of the world do you come from? Where was you brought up, that's what I want to know? Didn't they teach you nothing? No, you can't have ice in cider, nobody has bloody ice in cider, you drink it like it comes or don't bother.' 'Er, yes, quite, as it comes,' agreed the new boy meekly, the pub customers hanging on every word and heaving with merriment whilst the landlord returned to his crib game on the end of the bar, apologising, 'Sorry about that, chaps, you get these fellas that can't make their minds up what they wants.'

New landladies often resent the weeks of relentless toil without a day off here and there. Where they came from, beauty salons adver-tised in the local paper a day of relaxation and pampering. Looking at the country newspaper the only heading to leap out is Best Prices paid for fat cows, plain cows and bulling heifers. There are no exotic